THE DIARY OF A DOG

The life and times of a retired racing greyhound

Bandit

Illustrations Viv Levy

Transcription Robert Powell

Published in the United Kingdom by Fieldguard Ltd.,
Norley Farm, Horsham Road,
Cranleigh, Surrey GU6 8EH
01483 275182   info@fieldguard.com

Printed by Nightingale Press Ltd.,
Newark Close, Royston, Hertfordhsire SG8 5HL
01763 248393   studio@nightingalepress.co.uk

Layout and design by Frank Jones

A CIP record of this book is available from the British Library

First printed July 2013

Royalties apportioned to:
Celia Cross Greyhound Rescue, Sun Valley Kennels,
Shere Road, West Clandon, Surrey GU4 8SH
01483 222832   info@celiacross.org.uk
Charity Number 1020383

ISBN 978-0-9926052-0-9

The Diary of a Dog

For Danny the Sloughi, Judy the Border collie

GLOSSARY

Baby Jumping	Joey Kangaroo
BBT	Labrador
Biddy	Golden Retriever
BLCTH	Poodle
BWT	Rabbit
BSH	Jack Russell Terrier
Bundle	Play
Burn-up	Race
Cluckers	Chickens
Excitable dogs	Afghan, Saluki X lurcher, Whippet
FB&W	Husky
Gardening/Mining	digging in beds/digging in the lawn
Golden Hair & Floppy Ears	Golden Retriever
Large black and tan	German shepherd
Livery	Thoroughbred/Owner
LLH	Working Cocker Spaniel
Longhairs	King Charles' Spaniel
Longhair ears and tail	Saluki X Lurcher
Longhair long ears	Cocker Spaniel
#2	Defecate
Nuts	Complete dog feed pellets
Two Horses	Racing American Quarter Horses
SC/Slobber Chops	Bull Mastiff
SLLH	Long Haired Dachshund
Small furry	Heinz 57 rescue
Small and furry	Electric rabbit or small animals in general
Snarling snappy	Chihuahua
Spitting small furry	Cat
Tiny little bouncy	Griffon
Very large black (Hair dryer)	Labradoodle
Very large with silky hair	Borzoi X lurcher
Willow	Whippet X lurcher

The Gadabout, Idiot, Breadwinner, Moron, Panicking Percy, Mr Mop, Florence Nightingale, Mr McGoo, Clueless, Coronary Candidate.   *Bertie*

FOREWORD

Now let's get it straight from the off. Since retirement one no longer leads a varied, if solitary life. Actually, truth to tell it is pretty humdrum nowadays but I'll not fall into the same trap as Bertie did. He once kept a diary when very young and every day studiously started it with 'did usual things' only, reading the diary 65 years later he'd forgotten what the 'usual things' were. Of course, at the time it was quite logical for he knew what the 'usual things' were as he'd never done anything else so why repeat them?

On reading a first draft of this diary an ex friend commented on my vivid imagination. Recording facts for the future is a diary. Writing from an active imagination is fiction. This is a diary. Oh sometimes I have bent detail to help it flow but it is still all based on fact. Nothing made up.

We had better get it clear as well that, like Madonna and Prince, I am just Bandit. No need of a surname, for I don't belong to anyone. It was I who chose where I wished to live, not the other way around. It's the Willows (my housemate) of this world who have owners and 'belong'.

There are a great number of people who deserve thanks for my present contented circumstances, not least the caring people at the Greyhound Rescue Centre, but my greatest debt is to my loving family.

That is Willow for her companionship; and Bertie for sharing his home; while The Housekeeper never complains at the mess; nor the Bookkeeper at my costs; or the Salesman, Warehouseman and Livery lady for all the inconvenience to which I subject them on a regular basis.

Memoires and autobiographies can be seriously dull so I hope this one bucks that trend because I am not trying to justify any past mistakes or actions, but attempting to open the window on the world from a dog's view, well mine at any rate.

Bandit
MMXIII

Mutt - dog

CHAPTER 1

Monday January 1st

Well today is my birthday and I am officially four. As Molesworth* would say "any fule kno *[sic]*" that all high born greyhounds have their birthdays on the 1st January. It's tattooed in our ears. That also tells that my real name is Brendan but my new name since coming here is Bandit – long story don't ask.

* *'How to Be Topp'* books. Geoffrey Willans.

Didn't do much today for the Gadabout was out last night and seemed disinclined to do anything except feed us, his face, sleep and muck out the horses. It suited me fine as I am a bit under the weather anyway what with the stitches from my op and a wonky front leg. Bored with him snoring away in the middle of the day so, to amuse myself, I shredded a bog roll. Bertie is so insensitive for eventually dragged himself to bed at midnight when we had been desperate for some peace and quiet since about 8, but that's humans for you. Think of no one but themselves. Oh he did give us both a long cuddle – sort of Danegeld I suppose.

Tuesday

Bank holiday today, so gardener in him started messing around in the garden, for it was bright and sunny. Quite warm so Willow and I ran a bit – quite a lot actually. It's so nice for we have a large garden of lawns – amend, grassy field posing as lawns – that run around the entire house. There are just enough obstacles like flower beds, fences, drive, banks and a terrace to add variety and it is an almost perfect, well 'interesting', mini running place. Now we have 32 acres so I don't know why he doesn't make the garden into a decent size so I can really apply the afterburners – why I have a gammy leg, of course, what with all this trying to avoid things as well as get away from Willow. Pains me to admit it but she is far more agile than I. But then she would be for she has stumps for legs. A lot of sheepdog in her methinks. Then I lay and soaked up the sun while Willow did some gardening too, mainly mining the lawn and she also did a bit of weeding only gardener seemed to think that they should have stayed and got very cross. She doesn't know how to handle him so slunk off to her bed in a huff, tail between her legs.

Wednesday

Bertie went back to work today so we had peace and I managed a solid five hours testing the comfort of my bed again. It was just as comfortable as I'd remembered thank goodness. Mind you, was taken short so went in the utility room. Well all my life I've lived in kennels with little human interference in how I conduct myself so it is eat, drink, pee in the run. Well here there isn't a run so if no outside doors are open the next best thing is the utility room. Besides the poor sap just mops it up with an inane grin on his face. Think he has a conscience about the after – effects of my op for I still find it a strain when peeing. Anywhere else he tends to the shirty with much wielding of towels, awful smelling fluids from under the sink and furious scrubbing with hairy brushes. Black looks and incessant grumbling even when I come and lie beside him with an 'I am sorry' look on my face. Humans are so unpredictable.

Thursday

This morning the Idiot overslept so it was crash down the stairs and no good morning love-in for either of us but straight out to the fields. Willow, who is desperate for attention, was most put out. Don't think she had a particularly nice time at her previous home for she is very jumpy. In her case it wasn't her owner but the baby – babies always make a dog's life precarious domestically. Oh, Willow is a proper domestic and has 'owners'.

Icy North wind and I felt really cold. Upset me a bit because I need to have at least three #2's before I can run and doing them with this Arctic blast was no laughing matter. You try crapping in a wind tunnel at -7C. However, that out the way and a good blast to the fence where we raised a small & Bobbing White Tail (BWT) which was fun.

When I say 'we raised a BWT' that's not strictly true for I am no hunter, but just love an excuse to run as fast as possible. It's Willow who hunts but because she is a Shorty pants she cannot see them over the long grass so hops around like a Springbok relying on me to actually SEE them then, when we flush one, she is off and they usually end up dead. I do admire her for she grabs them and throws them in the air all in one movement. They land dead. Confirms that somewhere deep in her ancestry lurks sight hound blood but in every other way it is pretty well hidden. Strangely she has no further interest once they are dead so it is up to me to bring them to the house and sneak them into the dining room when no one is looking. Well he often eats there and is the pack leader (so he thinks when we all know it is really me) so it's the obvious place. The Housekeeper goes all girly when she finds one.

Then it was through the long grass (because the indolent bugger couldn't find anyone to make the hay last year and so just left it and it is now rank and evil smelling – riddled with fleas of course) and finally back to the warmth of the AGA and the usual parsimonious breakfast of a couple of spoons of yoghurt. Then I had another field trial of my bed. It was still comfortable.

Friday

Talking about hiding I am dark, heavily brindled and very quiet so can get away with murder for it is a perfect camouflage and I have found that if I stand just behind people I am truly invisible – mainly at dawn and dusk. Comes in particularly usefully at mucking-out time for I can lie in the hay keeping a check on him but invisibly. It's quite fun having him standing whistling and calling until he's exhausted. Can't see what he is fussing about for I know exactly where I am, right beside him as if with my handler at the running place. Still, it makes Willow feel important as she hares back from some distant corner of the garden.

Bit stymied as he has invested in a couple of those flashing collars now so he knows where we are at night even if not sure what we are actually doing. In an offbeat way, I slightly approve for it means I can keep tabs on Willow, so if the collar stops somewhere for a while tend to wander over to see what is holding her up. Think I'll need to blacken my white blaze – a dead giveaway. Happily my four elegant white paws can't be seen in grass.

Tuesday

And a red letter day for Wills because she was let off her lead on the walk for the first time. Oh apart from the first week we've never had leads walking in the oblong field but this was the first time 'when out'. Personally, I'm content to remain tied to the moron as he may wander off. Think that as his confidence increases it will be my turn without the lead. I suspect it is my coming to his whistle that bothers the fuss pot and delays this. Except when I'm in the mood, I tend to ignore him, especially if there is something really interesting to investigate.

Wednesday

At long last he's coming around to my way of doing things and has started letting us out for a final canter around the garden when the thing on the mantel hits its bell eight times. Then he can carry on playing his stupid computer to his heart's content while we get down to the serious business of studying the insides of our eye lids. Oh, this evening we went through the idiot routine of the flashing collars again as if we were going to stay out. Out in this freezing weather? Bertie's a moron.

Notwithstanding two visits to the Vet about my strained leg and some rather tasty anti-inflammatory pills, the swelling has not gone down. It is such a bind, for it means my going out on a lead most of the time, but often he forgets so I can slip in the occasional burn-up with Willow. That brings it back of course and I start limping again. Well seems that tomorrow it is the X-ray machine, so no food until then. I shredded a bog roll instead.

Oh, have I told you about my bog roll fetish? It was just something to do in idle moments or when I feel frustrated and want to take it out on something for they are soft and stretchy; and a bit of work on one produces my own snow. I suppose that when it snows outside there are people furiously shredding bog rolls, only theirs don't seem much good for they go away when it gets warmer.

Anyway back to the story. One day soon after we arrived, we all went to the top of the house for an afternoon nap, but I felt restless so had a little sortie. Happening upon the bathroom there was a basket of them; both smooth and crinkly ones. Took a smooth one into a spare bedroom and had a pleasant and productive half hour and then went back to finish my nap. There was no fall out, so the next time we went for a nap repeated the exercise on the landing with a crinkly and then returned etc. However Willow then went out and continued my handiwork and was still at it surrounded by snow when he got up. There was an absolute explosion of **NO**'s and poor Wills slunk downstairs. She refused to come up them again for some weeks. Having successfully demolished a few more I then rather spoiled matters by selecting a crinkly – much prefer the crinkly ones – from the basket in the back lavatory and bringing it to my bed right under his nose. The true bog roll shredder was revealed and so that is one harmless diversion now almost denied.

Thursday

And it was an early start. No breakfast and he took an indecent interest in my toilet arrangements. My goodness, it was bitterly cold with frozen ground, icy roads and the odd small snowflakes. Then it was a mad dash through the increasing blizzard to the big town. Not the big town where we shop nor the even bigger town over the hill, but the big town that is all narrow streets and one-way gyratory systems. Five miles out there was a traffic jam and we were late so Bertie took a long detour down very narrow lanes driving like a manic Mr Toad. We did arrive on time though and the surgery was all warm and cosy with lots of nice nurses billing and cooing over me (years of practice with handlers and kennel maids so I do have a certain 'something' and know just how to handle wimmin – you know the sort of thing, stand pressing against their legs all butch and masculine, looking away but give them a soulful over-the-shoulder glance, gets them every time).

In the waiting room I just lay contented in the middle of the room – and I can take up an indecent amount of space – with people stepping gingerly over me all the time but Willow was very put out for there was a snapping snarling little dog there as well. Willow doesn't rate small snappy dogs probably because she is small, well matronly, in build. Well, smaller than I anyway and that definitely gives her a complex. Have you noticed that people always have egos in inverse proportion to their size?

Now back to the X-ray. They eventually took me through to a room full of comfy cages so, never one to miss a trick, I had to test out one of the larger ones. Hmm, it was good so I curled up contentedly. Snarling, snappy came into one of the smaller ones on the next floor. Then they came and gave me that little prick in my leg that usually means slipping into Morpheus; it did, so I never actually saw this mythical beast the X-ray machine. A real bugger because I like to inspect everything. I woke feeling very woozy indeed. Definitely groggy and the pins had minds of their own.

In due course he and Willow turned up and out we went – only when he opened the door to the surgery there was a blizzard raging, temperature well below freezing and snow some inches deep. Not for me! I turned back into the nice warm surgery, and refused to move. Then the ultimate indignity, for he scooped me up and carried me to the car.

Did I tell you about us and cars? Well, all my life I have been lifted in and out of transport and see not the slightest reason to give up the practice. Besides, I like it for in my professional life it was the one time I ever had really close human contact. I taught Willow that on day one. When we got to the car, he was in a mess for he could not unlock it and lift the door as he was holding Willow's lead and me. He callously dropped me into the snow and then had the nerve to ask us to jump up. *Moi*!? Happily we'd agreed from day one that neither of us would do any such thing so he had to do it. There were waves of bad vibes from him.

The journey home through the thick driving snow appeared to be a bit of a nightmare. At least I think it was for I was still drowsy and in quite a fog about what was happening. It wasn't our car, for that will go through anything, but the other fools on the road. People seem to lose all reason when there's a bit of snow about. You can see them: engines screaming, tyres flailing and the car just sits doing nothing except go in the opposite direction, or worse still, just sits. Twice he stopped and gave mini-driving lessons. One woman was overwhelmed with gratitude and all he'd done was tell her to put it into a high gear, lift the clutch and not touch the exhilarator.

Home and he decided I needed to eat something – the very last thing on my mind. Have some lovely yoghurt; no thanks. Well, some milk; perish the thought. What about some scrambled egg? Definitely not! He must have got that in for we are a no egg house for he can't cook eggs. Some of your favourite mackerel in tomato sauce; over my dead body. Then, the ultimate irresistible option – some nuts soaked in vegetable oil. Now that is lip-smacking ambrosia. Had a desultory mouthful, thought about it for a few minutes, saw him add lashings more oil so felt duty bound to finish them off as he had gone to so much trouble. Actually it was just what was needed for felt replete and comfortable so snuggled down into my bed, he pulled the blanket over me and that was it until the morning. Oh, except that I did relieve myself in the utility room in the middle of the night when he came down for his midnight snack. He allowed it without demur. Actually I don't think he even noticed. Not the sharpest knife in the box at that time of night.

CHAPTER 2

Saturday

I'm feeling much more my old self. The snow is very deep and to our joy we were let out first thing. Of course I couldn't do much running, but Willow went wild and kept rolling in it, then using her nose as a snow plough. Still, I did manage a couple of circuits of the garden at full speed which was great fun with snow flying everywhere plus, of course, a goodly amount of rolling.

Writing this it is midnight and the coronary candidate has just thrown away his second empty fag packet of the day. He's smoking far too much so it's no wonder he puffs around our short blast in the fields first thing. More often than not he just stands coughing his heart out – I bet that tomorrow we are in for a mammoth session. On long walks he seriously labours but then, I don't mind that as not really into exercise myself beyond a few quick blasts around the garden. It's poor Willow who suffers, for she is more your day-long hikes type. She should have been a working dog of course, except that she's too thick. Oh, don't get me wrong I really do like our daily walks with so much to investigate plus the occasional small and furry (or feathered) to chase. More about walks anon.

Sunday

It was as I predicted, for he could hardly move this morning and was just as bad when we went for our afternoon walk. All that coughing and hacking is just so tedious. Well we don't choose the walks so he has no one to blame but himself for he chose one of our favourites. We have a very old building with stones around it perched on top of a steep hill surrounded by lovely paths and woods; I think it is called a church. Actually it's the first thing you see coming out of the house onto the terrace at home. Well, in normal weather it is a hike; but with a foot of snow? That's the walk he chose. Now we can circle the building from lower down the hill and that usually takes an hour but without that killing last incline to bother about. Not today, it was straight to the top. I thought he was going to pass out but we got there and he sat on a bench and had a fag would you believe! Looked like death too. Well we were pleased for it allowed us to play wonderful games in the snow until I bumped my leg on a hidden root and it gave me gyp again.

Tuesday

Did I tell you that we have only been here a short while; no? Oh sorry. You see he is a horse person rather than a dog one – been breeding horses forever and still treats us like very little ones. He walks the dogs at the local Greyhound Rescue Centre every Friday and had been becoming steadily more broody over the past few months; but every time he fell for one there were reasons why they were unsuitable. Then a shipment came in from across the sea and he took to a little lurcher because he was the spit of his previous sight hound. It was very young and bouncy. They said 'no' but look next door at this laid back small greyhound that came in as well – me of course. At the time I was asleep on the floor rather than the heated bed and could not be bothered. Well I'd had a fraught few weeks learning about the outside world so was thankful for a full belly and solitude.

Seems he can only consider small dogs because of the roof line of the car. It's called a sports estate which means that, as in all compromises, it does neither particularly well. There is a proper load area at the back that can take a kitchen sink but with a low roof line so even I, slight as I am, find my back brushing it when standing. Willow has no trouble but then she is SHORT. Any normal person would get the basics right beforehand but then, he's not normal. Vague and impractical are probably the right epithets to describe him. Still, I'll admit that the car is extremely comfortable, takes glutinous ploughed fields in its stride and it is fast. I suppose there is some compensation, for being so low generally it means that Wills can sit comfortably in the boot watching the world go by.

Next day he returned with the Nephew, and tried to bully him to take me. So, out Nephew and I went to the field and, let loose, I ran around him fit to burst but there wasn't anything between us, nor was he in a mood to play. Back to the kennels and that was when I met Bertie for the first time. Instantly recognised a fellow loner and rather took to him for he was reserved and slow. Decided he should be my person so made a fuss of him, even mounting his leg to much all round merriment. I'll give you more about all that anon.

Oh, I should explain the name. I think of him as a *Bertie* for he can be such a *berk* at times; and, as you'll have noticed, I revel in alliteration.

One of Bertie's friends came to meet us today. The friend is very arty and smelt of dog and was gentle and nice and she knew just where to tickle, besides I could feel that electricity between them the same as he has with Willow, me, the Nephew, the House-keeper, the Bookkeeper, the Salesman, the Warehouseman, and Distinguished lady. She adored Wills, Arty I mean. Have I said that Wills is a matronly sort? Very pretty in an urban domestic pet sort of way and does all the expected over-excited doggy things that people like. Perhaps I am being a bit harsh for she actually is stunning but in a doggy rather than sight hound way. She's small, curvaceous, has mascara around her eyes. In human terms she'd be a lady of a certain age who'd kept her looks but with bust, bum and brown brogues. She's always busy and fussing.

Arty friend was not so sure about me though, for a lowering, reserved greyhound can be intimidating so I allayed her anxiety by going to bed and lying on my back, feet in the air. Apart from being supremely comfortable that tends to disarm them for it looks ridiculous. I think she and himself 'do' arty things together for they never stopped talking about 'seeing this' or 'when should they go to that' and 'what a pity they missed the other'. Anyway the respite allowed me a few moments of shut eye. There was talk of taking us and her two mutts for a walk but that was abandoned when it was pointed out that my bad leg and having to be on a lead would restrict things.

Wednesday

Perhaps a little dissertation to get things into perspective wouldn't go amiss. Willow and I are nominally sight hounds. That is, dogs who hunt by sight. We see something moving, we go for it as fast as we can. Now in Wills case, she was born to be a house pet so she has a lot of doggy blood in her and doesn't look or behave much like a sight hound BUT she can still run and her hunting instincts are second to none. She catches and kills.

Willow has lived all her life as a domestic dog, so does all the things domestic dogs do like coming when called, sitting and walking to heel, jumping on furniture, riding in cars, gardening, mining (the lawn is now a series of spoil heaps) and generally being a bore sucking up to people; all things of which I heartily disapprove, so demeaning don't you think? She's savvy in the ways of the world and has strong homing instincts. She cannot relax in case she is missing something – amend could not for she is slowly learning relaxation from me. I'm sure I've already mentioned that Wills is a slow learner. Ditto that she is small? Coming here was a great shock for all of a sudden no furniture to jump on, no sleeping on beds, or riding on the back seat of the car and no walking through doors first. She felt mightily affronted and humiliated. It took her weeks to get over it.

While neither of us could, by the remotest description be called guard dogs she is very vocal and good at warning. She can hear the front gate latch or the crunch of wheels on the gravel and runs to the door with her 'there's someone arriving' whimper. As a good domestic she can also ask to go out, something for which I see not the slightest need. Oh, did I mention she is a frenetic tail wagger? I am more the slow-burner type. I have a magnificent smile I employ all the time which is both unusual and devastating so the tail department can be confined to a few slow approximations if I am particularly pleased or wish to ram a point home. What I certainly don't do is keep it between my legs – so unbecoming don't you feel? Many people tend towards inattentiveness you know so the slow-burn is just right. Tells them I'm pleased but reserved so don't get too chummy.

In comparison to Wills, I am of patrician persuasion reaching back thousands of years and untarnished by other blood. It is rumoured that we were the first dogs and we are built for one goal – to run very fast. I and my immediate ancestors originated in a very green and lush country across the water where most of the greyhounds in the world live. My parents and grandparents all ran. I was born and until I came here had lived all my life in a kennel. It was pretty solitary, for there is the kennel with run attached and that is where you live until someone comes and takes you in a vehicle to another kennel; so I quickly learned to always lie down in the vehicle as that settles the stomach. There, someone else pops you into another kennel. Then the handler comes and walks you around a ring and pops you into a trap. The trap opens and there is something small and furry haring away from you. Instinctively you give chase even though you'll never actually catch it. Then it goes and you stop running and wander aimlessly around until the handler comes and takes you back to the kennel. Then back in the vehicle and back to original kennel. Seen one kennel you've seen them all. Met one handler met them all. This walking beside them thing beforehand seems rather important so I'm very good at that.

This way I met an awful lot of people, but only in passing. Someone comes and puts your feed – usually milk-soaked bread and water dishes down. Someone else takes you for a short walk every day, cleans out the kennels and removes #2's from the run and that's about it. No real 'home', no other dog friends, and no humans to latch onto.

I now know that I am clever; show me something once and, unlike doggy-dogs, it is hot wired for ever more and I can also think and calculate. I always felt that there must be more to life and longed for the opportunity to learn, so I'd be nice to any human who showed any interest in me. Of course, there was an awful lot of standing with the handler at the place where the small and furry ran, so I quickly learned that because I don't speak human and they don't speak dog, body language was the only means of communicating, and it paid dividends to stand leaning against the handler's leg as that bought attention and I was able to reciprocate. That's where I developed the doe-eyed-over-the-shoulder look that is so devastating.

So I am well travelled and gregarious. I LOVE people, but have little concept of being a dog or owning/belonging to anything. Hence no territorial inclinations, except my pit, and no urge to actually catch and kill anything. I will run after the small and furry and when it's lost I am lost as well for not a clue where I am, who I am meant to be with, or how to return to the starting point for that has always been done for me. There would be people there to take me where I was supposed to be.

Because I've never actually mixed with dogs I don't really know how to relate or play with them, but Willow and my new frenetic social life are taking care of that now. Equally, living in a home with a sole human is taking some getting used to, for my natural instincts are to wander and latch onto any human who comes my way, on the assumption that they will look after me. Bertie on the other hand, seems to be very territorial and sticks to one like a limpet. Gets very shirty when I wander. However, his saving grace is that he revels in routines, so we do know where we are.

Have had to educate myself and establish my own rules of conduct without any help/interference from dogs or humans; so up to now my horizons have been pretty circumspect and meagre. Now you see why I sleep a lot, can be bone-headed if asked to do something I don't like and am quite content with my own company for it is how my life has been since I was a puppy. Until now it is all I have ever known, my rules for an equable life being learned from experience, so my current learning curve is very steep indeed. While quite used to being manhandled I have learned to cry piteously when people 'tend' me, whether they are hurting me or not, just in case they do hurt. I also have zero hunting instincts for they have not been needed for generations. It has also produced an odd quirk for I am scared of nothing, but very wary of cars for they hurt. Have I told you about my foraging days? No? Another time then.

Well that's taken care of the background. If you're curious for further background a stamped addressed envelope would be fine – oh and a little something to eat would be appreciated. Have I mentioned that he can be a bit parsimonious on that score? Well he can and I am a fair old trencherman.

Sunday

And the Nephew came today, that's the one he tried to palm me off to, with his mutt that is supposed to be related to lions – whatever they are. Anything less lion-like it is hard to imagine. Now how to put this delicately? Well he, the dog not the Nephew, has a large flat face, vast neck and chest with rolls of spare flesh and nothing at the back, paws like plates and he wheezes. Don't rate him much for running is an alien concept as he is bred to knock people over with his VAST bulk. Think steam rollers. Well he barged in, and like all our visitors dived straight in and polished off our feed nuts and sprayed drinking water all over the floor for his big head cannot get into our dinky troughs. That's the problem with normal dogs: totally obsessed with their stomachs, and untidy to boot. We sight hounds, on the other hand, only graze when we are peckish. Couple of mouthfuls, quick slurp of water and that's it for the next few hours. Well in my case, pee as well; then that's it.

Anyway, Wills and I sort of tried to make friends, but neither of us really rated him for he just stood and watched us tantalise him. Willow grabbed his neck but there were such rolls of flesh she couldn't get a mouth hold and goad him, for one shake, and

Slobber Chops.

she went flying. I then ran in tight circles till I was blue in the face. There was some mild reaction then nothing. Utter Zilch. Complete Zero. He's a total waste of space.

Then we loaded into the car; bit of a squeeze but I managed to curl up tight in a corner of the boot while Wills and Slobber Chops sat and looked out at the passing scenery. Went to our least favourite place, because in this wet weather it is very slippery; but it's popular with the hoi polloi because there are stunning views across the County and you can see for miles and miles. Hundreds of dogs but no sight hounds. Quite a lot of doggy doo doo's – people are so filthy. Well we both added to it with much muttering from the bread winner as he fumbled with and tied up the poo bags while trying to hold me. Not the most co-ordinated person in the world.

I suppose I don't rate this particular walk for he always keeps me on the long lead there, so I have no chance to test out the lovely wide open spaces. It was cold enough for me to be wearing my coat, and I felt a bit of a pansy when everyone else was enjoying the bracing chill. It actually turned out to be quite a nice walk really because himself and the Nephew are close and never stopped talking, plus, I also enjoy the umbilical cord between us for the lead is one of those 25' jobbies so there's quite enough freedom. Thank goodness he failed to make the Nephew take me, for him and his mutt are well suited and I'd have been the odd one out. The drooler is built to plod and be a 40 Kilo door mat. I think he can trot but that's about it in the speed stakes; hopeless! Still, he and Wills enjoyed the walk together as she is built more along his lines – short and, um well built. Have I told you that she is more an endurance type? I looked on, quite content not to be taking part in their mindless wanderings, neither of them being particularly blessed in the grey cells department.

Tuesday

My leg is now back to normal, thank goodness; so had some pretty fancy gyrations and runs first thing. Because I am now fit enough to run far faster than her, Wills has taken to just standing and taunting me. I shoot off around the house, thinking she is following; only she just trots across the terrace to face me as I come zooming around from the other side. I've covered 100 yards and she but 10. Do that four times in a row and you're pretty puffed, while she is as fresh as a daisy. Perhaps she is cannier than I imagined. Actually, coming to think about it, she is very cute and quick thinking on a number of issues. When he goes to work I can sometimes get a bit het-up and have the need of a pee. Know it is frowned upon so do it in the kitchen or utility room then go to the back lavatory and lift a bog roll which I happily shred in the other room hoping the one infamy will divert his wrath away from the other. Never works for I still get it in the neck. Zero sense of humour for there is wild wielding of mops and dust pans with loads of grumbles as background music. Wills would never step out of line like that. That's my Calvary.

Wednesday

Today Housekeeper went to close the drive gate so we could play outside in safety; but I'd followed in my best camouflage mode, just behind her right leg where she couldn't see me, and slipped to the other side when she wasn't looking. Later, she went berserk trying to find me, but, of course, I was the other side of the gate, so couldn't come. I'd been through the yard of the chichi offices to the road where a car bumped into me and nicked my leg rather painfully; so high-tailed it home, only found I couldn't get through the gate. She mopped it up and canoodled fondly for hours, for she was mightily upset.

I enjoyed the fuss, and found standing on three legs with the 'wounded' one dangling produced an awful lot of clucking sympathy. Blood everywhere of course. He came home and put on horse wound powder. Boy did that sting. I cried in pain and retired to my sick bed and tried to lick it off. Wonderful result, for that led to some serious fussing. So there was more of the stingy stuff, a plaster and some Vetwrap. Actually, it felt OK but continued the hangdog look and that produced all sorts of tasty morsels and much cuddling. He did curl up in bed with me for a while. Think I like being a hypochondriac but I am definitely never going to go to the road again, and that's cast in stone.

Thursday

I couldn't help but persistently lick the Vetwrap so he cut it off – piteous crying from me of course, just in case he hurt me. He decided we should visit my second home - so off we went to the Vet. Now this is not the place where I went for the X-ray but the local emporium, and it has a large reception room with free standing shelves in the middle full of doggy things. As usual, I inspected everything, and at the end by the counter was a box of pigs' ears - just at nose height. Have you ever eaten pigs' ears? To die for, they are so delicious! Quietly lifted one while he was flirting with the receptionist and refused to give it up, but the receptionist is VERY persuasive and promised I could have it back when we came out. Vet tut-tutted a bit and gave Bertie some pills. Good as her word, I got my pigs' ear back from the receptionist and happily demolished it coming home. In fact, there was a bonus, for Idiot felt guilty and bought another two which Wills and I had later.

Unlike the anti-inflammatory ones, these pills are vile and I refused to have them. He tried them in butter, peanut butter, tomato ketchup, cream, condensed milk, yoghurt, oil, meat and my feed. The walking dust-bin kindly helped me out. Finally, when we were down to the last three he learned how to do it with no option but to drop it down the back of my throat and rub it until I swallowed. Wonder where he learned that?

CHAPTER 3

Monday

On today's walk we flushed a vixen. Great fun, and Wills nearly caught her too, but it was in the commercial woods with lots of toppings all over the place making running difficult. Certain person became apoplectic with anxiety, whistling, calling and generally making a fuss to which we took not the slightest notice of course. Eventually took pity on him, and came trotting back, to his evident relief. Wills is learning that it pays not to be so instantly obedient. I'm much more laid back. If I do hear him (when the mist is down I don't of course) then I respond only when I've finished what I am doing with plenty of side excursions on the way. The secret is to put your head down when still a fair distance off and come back full tilt with a grin all over your face as if he was the only person in the world and you missed him. He's slowly learning. Did I mention that he's not all that quick on the uptake - that unlike normal dogs I do have memory banks and prioritise. Problem being that Wills is impetuous has the memory of a sieve and can't smile so she is often scolded.

Friday

I don't like Fridays much for he has now stopped going into work and does other things instead, like rushing aimlessly around in his car, finally ending up at home a heaving mass of anxiety. Then, he chucks our lunch down and munches through some foul concoction while downing a cup of coffee and lighting up, and then it is off again for the next three hours. I think he must be moonlighting at the Greyhound Rescue Centre, for he always comes back smelling of strange dogs. Us hard-done-by types get not only scant attention on Fridays, but no walks either.

Just to compound it, he often leaves us alone in the evening, for another of his lady friends comes and they go and play games somewhere. I invariably register my disapproval in the usual way. Bertie is so thick, for all he need do is close the bog door so I can't get at the rolls, after all the Housekeeper does. She even leaves the mop soaking in some evil smelling stuff ready for any puddles.

Sometimes it is here which is bearable, for a table is set up in the middle of the sitting room with four chairs and the little square tables from the drawing room beside them. Beforehand, he fusses in the kitchen doing something we aren't allowed to see – making human eats of course. He's transparent. Then, Game friend (who is a small but very nice and brusque lady with a thick 'different' accent but smells of dog) and another couple arrive and they just sit at the table with little square things in their hands; one can feel the tension so it must involve guile and brains. Willow can't bear the crowd, so retires to bed but I am happy for there are a couple of duvets down in the sitting room so I can curl up on the one where he is still in view and see if I am able to sleep.

Oddly, I can, for it is a fairly silent game. I will get up occasionally, have a good stretch and mosey around being sociable with each of them, inspecting what's on the small tables and giving some of the nibbles a taster's lick or slurp out of a glass that presents itself – have I mentioned that I like alcohol?

Unusual to see alcohol here for The Idiot doesn't drink. Often, one of them just sits there doing nothing; perfect opportunity for a mini love-in, and they duly oblige. Given my upbringing I'm not fussy who I do it with and they seem flattered with the attention, but Game is the best, for she does it so knowingly. Of course, my sensual silky hair helps enormously.

Wednesday

And we had a visitation from some of his relations with their very young baby + their bouncy black thief and a little black longhair with not such long ears. Baby just lay gurgling, so boring, and they all went into the drawing room for tea, leaving the four of us to get on together. I think that Little Black Longhair felt a bit overwhelmed by our attention for she certainly could run, but tended to snap when Wills wanted to play rough. Wills was attempting her throw her in the air to land dead routine but LBL was a little too heavy and squirmy for that. She was also intimidated by my size and the fact that I have not yet quite learned how to cope with domestic dogs.

The BBT wanted no part of socialising but made strenuous attempts to get into our feed bin, notwithstanding the heap of clothes that had been piled on top to deter her. Bouncy Black Thieves are single minded – their stomachs rule their entire thought processes to the exclusion of everything else, so she was a total wash out. She managed the bin alright, but unfortunately for her it was only a third full and her neck was too short. Very frustrated, so she demolished the tail ends of our chews and bones instead. She got very nasty when I politely tried to move my bone away into safe keeping. Visit not an unqualified success, and I am coming to the conclusion that I have little patience, beyond social politeness, with domestic doggy-dogs.

Friday

Now this morning a jolly lady with a smile like the Cheshire cat tramped through the deep snow with her mutt to meet us. She, the mutt I mean not the Cheshire cat, was a nice old biddy with long golden hair and big floppy ears, and we all rather took to each other, although any running or playing was out of the question for we respected her maturity. One is not totally insensitive. I've a feeling she's the one that lives at the bottom of the oblong field for sometimes on our morning apology for a walk we hear her – the Cheshire cat not the old biddy - calling to Bertie. Anyway after the usual courtesies, she took old Biddy for a short walk down the oblong field, and Wills and I joined them. It was sedate fun which we thoroughly enjoyed. Out of respect to Biddy, I hopped and skipped around them like a loony rather than running. It also placated Cheshire cat, for she felt a bit responsible for us. Wills vainly tried to get Biddy interested in a spot of mild hunting, but she was having none of it. I don't think she's a hunter but do think that she, Biddy not the Cheshire cat, is about to become a rather regular companion and that is nice for one does need a social life. Something about not living on bread and water alone stirs at the back of my mind.

Monday

Today the Housekeeper decided to clean up our bed, and, hoorah, she finally got it supremely comfortable. As it is so important, I'd better explain our bed situation. Our house isn't very large but has lots of similar sized rooms including the kitchen. Because the magpie has so much 'stuff', space is a bit of a premium and nowhere more so than in the kitchen. However, the kitchen does have a handy sized alcove where the fire place used to be and my bed, or at least the one I chose, is in there, not quite a perfect fit though, for the bed is a few inches short so the gap is filled with one of those doggy mats rolled up. Willow's bed is at right angles and sticks out into the kitchen, so the two beds are sort of L-shaped. Filling the inside of the L is a thin mattress, so we have over flow when both stretched out–after all we can each stretch to 5 feet when laid out. Beyond is the chopping table as a sort of protective peninsula where the cutlery and all the important house papers live. You know the sort of thing: open calendar, entertaining book, and things to be answered. Then a mere pace off to the right is the actual kitchen table where he sits with his bloody computer. It's nice for the three of us are where we want to be but still very close to each other. I don't really like to have him out of sight for you never know what sort of mischief he might be up to. Besides which, we both like looking at him while we're thinking how to make his life more interesting. Wills is very nervy and reacts to every twitch he makes while I just open an eye to check what's happening. I'll give you more about the domestics anon.

Normally, Housekeeper just leaves our comfy mess, but this time she had everything out. Cleaned the area, disposed of discarded bit of this and that, and put it all back. Didn't know what to do with the blankets so folded them up and dropped them onto the ends of the beds. In my case, it makes the most superb pillow. Thoroughly approve. Wills was not so grateful for she put the thin bed in Willows place and her bed in the overflow place AND she folded Will's blanket inside out. She's sloppy that way, not good on details. Well he sorted that, and I've been in seventh heaven ever since. Wills likes it too, so sometimes usurps mine, but I have obvious but courteous ways of persuading her back to HER bed.

Actually I REALLY like my bed for it is surrounded by three walls and this allows me to indulge in my 'feet-in-the-air' pose that's so comfortable – practical point for those walls also exclude the draughts to which the house is prone. Bertie has spent hours tracking down the sources and applying sticky tape but they still remain. Latest victim was the unused front door at the other end of the house. It did nothing for the kitchen draughts, but wonders in the sitting room which has always been an iceberg. We can finally watch TV without getting chilblains. In fact, the room is almost cosy for the first time ever.

Wednesday

I did my leg in again today while trying to execute a particularly tricky manoeuvre involving the sleeper wall and the gravel drive. Came off alright but felt the twinge and sure enough, up it came. As usual, he dithered even though I kept telling him that this time it was really hurting.

Thursday

He finally took the hints - and they could not have been louder – so we are booked into my second home on Saturday. In the mean time managed to drag myself around a walk put on by the Cheshire cat and Biddy. They came in their car with Biddy in the front foot well for she is now too old to get over the tailgate. We were supposed to do that but it was a cliff face, so both did our pathetic look and he lifted us in. I think this lifting onto tailgates is becoming something of an issue – nothing concrete you understand, but just a little *je ne sais quoi* when it happens. Anyway, approved of where we ended up, for it is one of our favourite areas for walking.

Because our village is in a valley, the cricket ground is up on top of the hill around the heath. There are nice woods beside, and they lead to the woods where we raised the vixen, so all in all enjoyable variety on all our walks there. Well, Biddy showed us new parts which we'd not known about, so it was into the woods and then down to the butterfly field. There was a stile with a trap for dogs to go through. It quite reminded me of old times going through it. As in my professional days, I resisted going in, so was unceremoniously booted through. Some things never change. The field is a butterfly sanctuary, so wide open, and a wonderful place to have a burst so I duly obliged by showing the Cheshire cat what I can manage. She was duly impressed. Even when my leg is gammy I can still run – it's just walking that is such a (literal) pain. Then through some delightful bluebell woods – you could see the first shoots – onto the heath which I love because the heather makes me invisible, and back over the cricket pitch to the car where we once again went through the charade of getting in. A really lovely and varied walk it was too and I think Biddy enjoyed sharing it with us.

CHAPTER 4

Saturday

Today hit the jack pot, every gold medal ever awarded, broke the casino and, like those German students in days gone by, I am going to have lifetime scars for my efforts. Perhaps I'd better take you through the day one step at a time – don't want to over-tax your grey matter too much do we?

Well, in setting off for the surgery, I kicked up a fuss and refused to go up the snazzy ramp he has been lent by the dog trainer. Have I told you about her visit? No? Well another time then. Because it was cold and drizzling, eventually he gave in and lifted me untidily into the car. Smarty pants had already jumped in because there were treats flying around. Of course, because she only thinks of herself she kept getting in the way trying to prize a treat out of his hand. What with holding Wills at bay, trying to goad me, keeping some treats and the ramp he got into a right pickle. Then we finally got to the vets – late.

Now let me explain; the vet is on a busy road, but we park down the side. Well he opened the tail gate and I saw all those cars whizzing past in the icy rain and thought 'over my dead body' so just stayed lying in the comfortable boot. Ramp out, no good; cajoling, nothing; so then he scooped me out and onto the ground where I just stood transfixed. Tried to lead me away from the entrance so obliged him, but the moment we turned around I froze. Ended up with him carrying me to the door of the vets, and even there I was all for running back to the car, except that a whoosh of warm air came out so in I went. Utter disgrace: no pigs' ears but only very down market cows' ears. Frightfully Costa Brava. This time it was a nice Scottish man who gave some more of those nice pills. It does seem there is a problem – a left - over from my professional life. Nothing operable, but until my muscles have hardened up again it will flare up from time to time when I am working hard. Anyway, that sorted, and time to leave.

I had not the slightest intention of going towards the door and those whizzing cars, so the nice Scottish man became a not so nice Scottish man and first pushed me with his knee and then very firmly manhandled me right to the car where I scampered up the ramp with pleasure, the foregoing being so undignified. Happily all that lifting has probably done clueless' back in again. You try holding 28 kilo of floppy dog with legs everywhere. It is no joke I can tell you.

Home, peace, lunch and then he waited for Arty to come, thoughtfully opening the gate for her. We were supposed to be going for a walk. Well, it was so miserable that we stayed in the kitchen as she read the proof of what I've written so far; while he read something she had bought over. Then Wills decided she wanted to go out for a pee so he thoughtlessly opened the door for us both and went back to his reading.

Of course, with the gate open and the BWT field beckoning enticingly, before you could say 'boo' we were there. Being so dense, Wills led the way for I long ago twigged that going through the gate is an absolute no. For some reason he gets very shirty if we do, and I really don't like upsetting him. Instantly saw a BWT which we raised, only it went through the barbed wire into the bulrush-strewn swamp beyond and, naturally, I followed, cutting both my ears, a leg and my scalp in the process. Willow, as usual, unscathed, but then did I ever mention it but she is, well being kind, a bit short shall we say. I seemed to end up in a small river with lots of dead trees all over the place, not to my liking at all and no obvious way out – after a hunt my Sat. Nav. goes on the blink you know, and I get all disoriented. I could hear him calling in a panicky way, with Willow dutifully beside him, for her Sat. Nav. is unerring.

In fact, he must have caught a glimpse of me through the vegetation. Smart of him, for all this foliage was a perfect camouflage. Well he certainly wasn't dressed for outside, but I take my hat off, for he scrambled through the barbed wire and swamp to the low supposedly 'dog proof' fence of the Duchess's garden (our next door neighbour was a Duchess and her grandson is our Landlord) where I had somehow ended up. Well, it may have kept her small and furry in but no match for me, or Willow, as it transpired.

Well, I stood on the lawn dripping blood from everywhere, and holding my paw up, for the barbed wire had skinned it, and it really did hurt. Wills started running up and down the other side of the barbed wire crying, but she was so upset that the two most important people in her life were elsewhere, she came through barbed wire and swamp (it is thick black goo and came up to her tummy so she was now a smelly mess) and stood with him one side and me the other. He lifted her over to join me and then went back to the house to don suitable clothes and shoes as his ones were ruined of course. I think he intended to grab our leads and go around by the road to the house, walk across the lawn and retrieve us but we weren't having any of it and I showed Wills the way out, thereby adding to my bleeding cuts and we arrived back at the house just as he was walking out. Jammy devil, she still had not a scratch. I think Wills is like one of those children who incite all their playmates to do naughty things but are careful to make sure that they are never caught themselves.

Naturally we walked into the utility room with my bleeding ear dropping blood everywhere but I did rather complicate the situation for not only was the blood pouring out but it stung: so I did the natural thing and shook my head, not once but repeatedly. Blood flew everywhere – up the walls, the doors, even the windows. Particularly pleasingly the Housekeeper had a lot of delicate white things drying on the clothes horse. Splattered. Then I added to it by coming into the kitchen and repeating the exercise again, and again, and again. The place looked like a slaughter house and, of course, Panicking Percy was in a blind frenzy.

Well, Arty was quite good and practical, for she asked where the cleaning stuff was but he just burbled nonsensically while trying to put a roller towel around my neck and make it stay. One shake and it was gone. Then he tried cotton buds and Vetwrap: ditto result, and lots more bleeding. She then rang the vet who was, of course, closed, but there was an emergency number, only he said it would have to be a house visit for the car would look like a cadaver wagon otherwise. It was she who suggested the whites should go into cold water. PP would never think of that.

In the middle of all this the salesman rang to say he had something to give Panicking Percy. Well the salesman's last wife was a Veterinary nurse so he, the salesman I mean for PP was way past rational thought, rang her and she gave some sensible advice on how to cope with my bloody ear. The sensible salesman then arbitrarily tied us up in the tiny veranda by the outside door where I could bleed to my heart's content without doing damage for congealed blood looks part of the pattern on the ironstone walls. Oh, there are the smart (visitors) back door, the plebs (the one we use) back door, and a couple of white windows for me to spray. Wills just sat and whimpered incessantly. She's become very vocal of late and, rather touchingly, most concerned about me. Well it takes two to tango, for I adore her.

Panicking Percy was despatched to the tack room in the stables for a roll of Gamgee. Then Salesman gently held my ear up with the Gamgee either side for a fairly long time, well, until the bleeding had almost stopped. He was very gentle and considerate with me and while holding my ear up he tried to wipe away the blood on my forehead and body. Think I like him a lot for we are very similar in outlook and he just seems to be an all round good egg.

By then, I was shivering with cold and reaction, so decided to have a power nap and lay on the bad ear which proved jolly good for it really did stop the bleeding. One shake and the Gamgee came away but left a film of cotton wool over the wounds. There we stayed while Mr Mop furiously washed down everything inside. I think the blood on the walls has stained the paintwork in some places.

Then it transpired he'd not yet mucked the stables out, so salesman and he went off to do a lick-and-a-promise job leaving us to freeze on the porch. I just slept, and Willow cried. Two and a half hours later he had virtually finished the cleaning when the Livery lady arrived, and, gentleman that I am, I got up to greet her. She was delightfully solicitous and very helpfully wiped away the cotton wool which instantly opened up the wounds again. More blood, but far less than before. Off they went to bring the nags in, and as he walked up the drive Arty arrived back with some sensible first aid. Well, by now it was raining quite hard and both of us really wanted to pee and clean ourselves in the wet grass, so off we went and both had delicious and repeated rolls. Actually, given the very short time he allowed, we did a pretty good job even though I say it myself but, my goodness, we were cold, so very happy when Panicking Percy called us in. Wills managed to wash away virtually all the black goo, although she smells something rotten.

Florence Nightingale then applied a pad and a small section of the thin bandage from the first aid which looked fine. One shake and it was off, so then he tried the rest of the thin bandage. Same result and this time he took no chances and applied a grown-up bandage. The works, the full bazooka, and I didn't even bother to try getting it off. One knows when to retreat. I was also feeling very tired indeed; must have been the shock of the whole thing, so took over Willow's bed and slept the sleep of the just, while Mr Mop continued the entire cleaning operation for a second time. It was very late when he finally popped something into the microwave.

Both an afternoon and evening of cleaning, and I can tell you the second session was pretty arbitrary – he had to do it though, as he has someone coming to a kitchen lunch tomorrow. Not the slightest attempt to clean either of us, of course. Now, having had a good sleep, a nice go at the nuts, and a drink, I was feeling much more myself and even tried to dislodge the bandage – but it is firmly there. Wonder if he'll try to get me to some emergency vet tomorrow for he has yet to actually give me a good going over to assess the damage? Bet we are only allowed out for our last pee of the evening on a lead.

I don't think he'll ever overlook closing the gate again for he is looking pretty drained and exhausted. Every bit his seventy mumble years. Think we may have stretched him beyond breaking point today, for he's eaten virtually nothing. For certain, he'll have a sleepless night. And I have a feeling that more angst is due tomorrow when he attempts to give us both a bath for the first time which I presume that he will.

Well, won my bet for we did have leads, only I refused to go out. Wonder if I'm what the medics term 'a bleeder'? That would account for needing a drip for three days after my op.

I feel rather sorry for PP, for his heart is in the right place even though he doesn't have a clue about most things. It is obvious that there was once a woman living here, for the house has that sort of feel. While a masculine house, it is very much NOT a bachelor pad. Actually, coming to think of it, when we first arrived, after showing us around, about the first thing he did was walk us to a place with a big building and lots of stones scattered around, where he started talking to a slab. One 'felt' things all around, particularly from that slab. Because we cannot use words animals tend towards the spiritual, you know.

Truth to tell, he is the first human who has ever loved me, and although I'm reserved in such matters, those feelings are mutual. Most of the time things go very right between us, and there is nothing I like more than being with him for he is my person, and I do try to acquiesce even if he plainly doesn't quite understand me. Did I tell you that he's a bit dense at times? After all, I did choose him as he's far too dithery to have chosen me. Something about for better or worse, but I probably drew the short straw on that score. There is that other saw about beds and lying, well mine is mighty comfortable at this moment, nighty night.

Bundling

Sunday

And this morning it feels very like "The Nightmare Song"*

> *But the darkness has passed, and it's daylight at last!*
> *The night has been long, ditto, ditto my song,*
> *And thank goodness they're both of them over!*
> * *'Iolanthe'* WS Gilbert

No sound of morning ablutions, and a very subdued PP came down smelling of embrocation – sure sign he strained his back yesterday. Wills smells like a sewer. 18 hours after the event my ear is still dripping blood – confirmation of my earlier thoughts of course. Still covered in caked blood around the neck region, leg REALLY sore, so I cannot say the world is a happier place.

Now this sad situation is a shame for there is one thing on which PP and I do agree, and that is that the glass is always half-full. Normally, he crashes through life with gay abandon, while I'm more the svelte cad in a silk dressing gown type. Today, we both are feeling that the glass is half *empty*. No smiles from me, and a definite weary frostiness about him, for he finally got to bed in the early hours. He looks frazzled, unkempt and VERY black. Barge poles methinks until the mood improves, warned Will. Suspect we will be confined to the servants' quarters for some time. Have I mentioned that we live in a rather smart house with bags of things about which visitors ooh and aah and then chatter about dementedly? The word 'artworks' keeps popping up. All I know is that they do nothing for either of us and get in the way.

That also means no dread bath; what a relief. Florence *did* finally get down on his knees and give me a detailed inspection.

Loved the close attention, and wondering if there is anything that necessitates another visit to my second home, for our car has cream insides and, like all men, the car is his pride and joy. He's still cleaning up, and Wills and I are keeping well out of the way of this ominous black cloud on legs. The visitor is due any moment, and he's done not a thing about lunch.

Thank goodness visitor arrived! She proved there was a sentient being under the black cloud, and brought him back to life. Well, he had to put on some sort of a show, for it is pretty obvious she's a dog person by the present she bought - crunchy treats! Somehow, goodies kept popping out of the AGA and fridge, followed by a lot of lip-smacking by both of them, and she stayed for ever. When she eventually went, he was back to his normal self, so we both made a great fuss of him while he mucked out the stables.

It was such fun the three of us being back together again, as The Great Marsh Adventure gradually recedes into history. Wills and I were both delirious with happiness. I helpfully assisted him filling the water bucket of the blind mare while Wills helped him get out the feed – I've taught her the delights of horse feed learned from my days of foraging. Have I told you about my foraging days? I'm sure I will in due course.

The gelding is skin and bone when usually he is a chub, so he's being given some particularly tasty feed at the moment. I prefer the blander stuff the blind mare has if it is soaked and, lo, there was a bucket of wet her feed for me to fill my boots. The food got wet because she's not in a stable, but in a sort of roped-off area, and the Idiot had put it under a hole in the roof. How daft can one be? In between, we played in the fairly heavy rain on the lawn, for one knows that mucking-out signals no walks today.

Well, being so wet it did slightly soften the mess in which we both were including the residual caked black goo from the swamp on Wills. So when we came in there was copious wielding of wet sponges, then vigorous rub-downs for each of us, followed by even more vigorous brushing. It was utter Bliss. Feel much fresher and that probably puts paid to the dread bath hanging over our heads as well, for Wills no longer smells of well-rotted vegetation. Florence finally noticed the great wire gashes on my bad front leg – why I had it dangling in the Duchess' garden - and the chunks of hair off my chest, other ear and both back legs. Told you he is slow. He'll not do anything, of course, for it's very difficult to stitch our legs, for the skin is so tightly stretched. It would be a different matter if I was a doggy-dog of course, but then, they're not built to be speed machines.

Tomorrow the Housekeeper will throw a major wobbly, for there is now a veritable mountain of washing. Last count: four roller towels and six washing-ups + all the assorted whites that had just been lovingly washed on Friday, and two bandages. That excludes his pants, shirt, jersey and anorak for they went into the basket upstairs. That's the one where I chewed the lid last month in a moment of idle forgetfulness. Feeling very satisfied after a useful day so, as Wills is already asleep IN BED.................

Monday

He over-slept again, and we're still confined to the servant's wing as Florence doesn't quite trust my ex-bleeding ear against the good furniture. Recently, our morning walks have reduced dramatically since he now starts off by going down to the barn and giving the nags their breakfast. Did I tell you that the chestnut is skin and bone? Well he, Florence I mean not the chestnut, has taken to giving them all breakfast – damn sight more generous than that he gives us too. So it's out the door, quick pee and down to the stables where I fill in the time by doing at least two #2's in places he can see. Today I was particularly clever for one was on the wide crack in the concrete floor just where everyone walks. He could only scoop up some and had to come back to the house for some thin gloves to get at the rest down the crack thereby reducing our otherwise truncated morning walk to a token once down the big field.

Luckily, Wills is always bouncing with energy, and invents sightings at the far end of the triangle field. So, being careful to duck without touching the electric fence - Wills has no need of course as she is so stunted - we have a quick burn-up chasing the mythical BWT. Clears the cobwebs and suits me perfectly. I wonder if my other home could reduce my legs by a couple of inches for it would make things like barbed wire and electric fences so much easier to negotiate at speed without being injured or zapped.

Why the rush in the morning? Well, I'd better explain. You see there are the blind mare and the chestnut gelding, and they have been stable mates for years and years except they don't actually like each other. They were in the same profession as me, you know. They are the fastest animal on earth over 400 yards, although to look at them now you'd never guess it. Enter stage left the livery. She and the chestnut are best mates, rather along the lines of Willow and I, and when the blind mare became blind she, the livery I mean, took great delight in acting as her minder in the fields. Now livery's person, a big jolly lady who Willow and I adore - has to get her son to college by 8.30. So its horses out at around 8-8.10 without fail. Like me, Florence is not a morning person and can barely drag himself from his pit at 7.30. He oversleeps an awful lot, which does nothing to improve the situation. He has a quick shave, comes down and gives us a brief 'morning' for a greeting. Then it's out for the so-called morning walk.

Well, it used to be out for a good half hour around the fields, but now we have this time-wasting diversion. It never occurs to the moron to get up earlier, so what suffers? The morning walk of course, now reduced to mere tokenism. I don't know how he has the gall. Apart from upsetting my toilet arrangements it suits me though for it does mean a few more minutes in bed and I heartily approve of that. It's just not done for a gentleman to stir before eight anyway.

Housekeeper has arrived and she just laughed at the residual carnage. What a brick and a ray of sunshine for if she spotted some congealed droplets that Mr McGoo had missed, she just laughed and with a merry wipe, chided him for having missed them as she vigorously rubbed them away. She was such a ray of sunshine after forty eight rather bleak hours that it almost blinded us.

CHAPTER 5

Tuesday

We awoke to snow. Not the big healthy stuff, but the thin
drizzly sort that is wet, clingy and cold. The morning canter was
not such fun, although Wills did her usual phantom sighting.
Think we may be in for another bad dose of snow to add to our
pleasure and his woes. Happier to test my warm bed though, and
this is exactly what I did – all day except for the walk. He had
to take us for a walk as we haven't had one for four days. It was
bitter and wet so he put on our coats which neither of us liked
one bit, so we kept shaking and I did manage to open up my ear
again.

I've been thinking about the Great Marsh Adventure. It is a
given that good comes out of adversity, and it has done so this
time in a big way for it has demonstrably bought the three of us
much closer than I imagined possible. It bought out depths of
feelings in each of us which none knew existed. We are now a
true pack of three equal people. Wills is much more relaxed and
concerned for the two chaps, and I now keep firm tabs on both of
them while he watches over us like a mother hen. I've dropped
my defensive, detached air of independence for, for the first time
ever, I am part of a pack and it is lovely. To me the glass isn't

half-full but brimming over. Same goes for Willow. Life couldn't be better, although a bit of sunshine and warmth wouldn't go amiss.

Wednesday

You know, Bertie's sense of humour has worn pretty thin after the marsh escapade. He's become quite snappy and is forever wetting a sponge and wiping my face and neck then the offending bit of wall or door. Rather like the attention, though, even if he isn't quite as gentle as one deserves.

I think I must have been the runt of my litter for I am quite a bit smaller than my contemporaries and my back end is definitely weak. While my hind legs are muscled they are not those gross muscle-bound body-builder ones that others seem to possess. At one running place there was one big chap who could barely walk – he was so gross. I think I like my svelte outline better, but there is one unfortunate side effect - it makes me appear slightly bandy legged - so the sobriquet 'Bandy Bandit' did rather stick at the Rescue Centre. Mind you this lightness at the back means that I bounce along and Bertie approves of that for, of course, when we are out walking my back end is all he sees of me. He must have had a dog previously that bounced.

We really shouldn't mention Wills' bum. Being kind she is 'well padded' and, of course, she just bustles untidily, no grace or *mouvement* while those little legs work as furiously as a windmill in a hurricane. She's busy busy busy just like the White Rabbit. Talking of 'rabbits' he is always on about the 'rabbit fence' but what he doesn't realise is that the fence to which I think he's alluding keeps most of the BWT's *out* and us *in* so we cannot get at them. Told you he's not all that bright.

Thursday

Now I feel that it's time for an outline regarding our domestic arrangements. We live on a farm, well, actually the farm house, because the main farm buildings are chichi offices full of long haired people with fancy cars who 'do' things in media and such stuff. Excluding the BWT and triangle fields which are the other side of the farm buildings, our property is oblong and flanked on two sides by the road.

We also have a large barn with the stables alongside. The barn and house are in the bottom right hand corner of the oblong but facing the road. As no one can stop on the road, the front gate and door are never used. In fact, the front door - the troublesome one with the draughts I mentioned - is now sealed up. The drive is through the farm buildings and comes to the two back doors. I think they work on the principle of if you can't have one of each then better to have two of one. The top right hand corner has the orchard and a large square fenced area where they teach the horses, but as it is never used one assumes that the horses know everything. Now here's an odd thing. With all this torrential rain we have been having the floor of the teaching area never floods. Oh it gets wet, but unlike everywhere else, there are never any actual puddles or lakes. That's very strange.

That area is now out of bounds, anyway, because the fence onto the road is porous and easy to get through. I did a couple of times and latched onto the closest person, usually people walking, and they bought me home. They always hand me back with accusing looks as if to say that he should know better.

The rest of the oblong is the big field where we walk every morning with the triangle field off to the left. The small & Bobbing White Tail field is at the end of the drive past the chichi offices. All the internal fences are electric bands; the ones nearest the house with BWT netting underneath so they are also supposedly dog-proof. However, the low wall at the front onto the road and the road fence as well are either low, like easily jumped low, or nonexistent. Before we came he did make strenuous attempts to make it all dog proof, but within hours I found escape routes. So he spent most of the Christmas break working to bung the holes up and in the process cut off the orchard and non-flooding area.

From that you'll divine that this diary does not start at the beginning, but from some while after our arrival. We were all a sort of Christmas present to each other but my official birthday seems a sensible day to start writing.

This road is quite a problem for while it's only a grown-up cart track, it is actually the only way to get from the big town where we shop to the big town with the X-ray but missing out the very big town over the hill which is always snarled with traffic. The road snakes in a large S around us so traffic has to go quite slowly. It also has a narrow pavement where we have a constant stream of walkers and hikers. All very earnest with their Norwegian walking sticks, sagging knapsacks and lurid coloured bobble hats. They come here because we are in the most glorious countryside with miles of walks all around – frankly, dog heaven. Oh I nearly forgot, at weekends we also have hordes and hordes of cyclists, because the road was part of not only the Tour de France but also the Olympics when they came to the country. Those were before our time so we missed them. Mind you, none of them do anything for us because they don't stop at the struggling village shop 100 yards away.

Because our house is on a slight hill, there are stunning views in every direction AND we get the full blast of any nasty winds, but that's compensated by lovely sunsets every evening.

Biddy

Friday

And let joy be unconfined, for today the Housekeeper found three tiny droplets of old blood and a bit of ear on the ceiling. That's some achievement for they are 8' high ceilings. Rather proud of myself. This morning a most unusual thing happened, for Bertie put on our walking collars first thing after breakfast - and that's never happened before. It was a lovely sunny and warm day, too, which is a great relief after all the cold and damp we have lived through over the past weeks. One felt that Spring, while not actually here yet, was just around the corner.

Then he went around to the front gate – the one onto the busy road – with the 'formal' leather leads and called us. Door mat went, of course, but I wasn't having any of it, so he chased me fruitlessly while I pranced around. Finally, he corralled me in the veranda and clipped me on. Then back to the front gate and I dug my heels in. NOT ONE STEP. He may be able to make a horse stand on its head, but so far as I'm concerned, forget the starting trap. He's not even at the running place.

I've taken against traffic you see and nothing on earth will make me go near it now. So, back and past the chichi offices where he had to drag me along the road until we came to the lane, and there were Biddy and the Cheshire cat. Over the road, and followed the most wonderful walk possible. There was so much to see and inspect. People's gardens; a working farm yard; a smelly garage with bits of cars lying around; steep banks; vast open fields; fields of stubble; woodlands; rusty barbed wire fences to negotiate and lots of varying woods. Oh, and two very steep hills as well. Finally we crossed the lane to the foot of the hill with the big building at the top and went down a steep path through a working coppice and along a secret river path through beech trees of quite wonderful beauty to Biddy's house. There we parted, and the hateful leads put on to be followed by a nightmare walk along the busy road to home. I really did not like that part and showed it. Pity, for it spoiled what had otherwise been a most tremendous walk which Biddy, Willow and I loved. It had been so good that my gammy leg even behaved.

Oh, and on the way we met two black walking barrels (BBTs) – you know the ones. They're what everyone either in the country, or pretending to live in the country own. Their presence hinting that their owners indulge in a 'sporting' country life. Big, bouncy, brainless, thieving, bereft of character and single mindedly concerned for their stomachs, but people dote on them for they are real domestics. Now I'm a pretty laid back sort and take life and dogs as they come but those two acted so *supérieur*. Like those chinless wonders who are too stupid to realise that they don't actually rule the world but still act as if they do. I was forced to put one of the Big Bouncy Thieves in its place and, coward that it is, it retreated and had nothing further to do with us; thank goodness, for he had been making lewd suggestions to Willow.

Not the behaviour of a gentleman.

When we arrived home a car turned up. We went to welcome the person but she foxed us by getting out of the wrong side; the driving place must have slipped during the journey.

At the top of the house is a mysterious room with an always closed door. I've often wondered what guilty secret was hidden behind that door; but today all was revealed – for it is empty, except for rows of cupboards and a table. The visitor went in and rummaged around, extracting hordes of clothes which she put in the back of the car. She explained that they were her 'English' clothes and that confirmed that she had come a long way. Spot of scratch lunch, and off she went – not before Wills had shown her how to go mining though.

From her body language, and the fact that he allowed her to roam freely around the house, I'd say she was pretty close to him. Still, as a host, one does have certain courtesies so I accompanied her upstairs and, gratifyingly, she managed to fall over me a couple of times when in the secret room. That settled, waved her off, closed the front gate, and all retired to some well earned sleep for it had been a busy day. Her visit, and the oddly timed walk, explained why he hadn't gone off doing his mysterious Friday afternoon doggy moonlighting.

I bet you're speculating how I know that I'm a greyhound. Well it's very simple, really, for it is one of my secondary names on a par with 'Boy', 'Chap', 'Fellow' – usually prefaced with 'Good', 'Old', 'My', 'Bad'. As it is never used except when talking to others, I can only come to that obvious conclusion. Willow has the same string of secondary names. Not a clue what make of dog Willow, Biddy, Slobber Chops, or any of the others are but greyhounds they are not.

Monday

Did I ever mention that in the sitting room we have a TV brooding in the corner? Oh sorry, for we do although we seldom use it. I think it came with the house for it looks as if it came out of the Ark and needs all sorts of mysterious stoking before it wakes up. It sits on top of a number of flashing boxes and there are loads of those little plastic bars with buttons on them which he presses furiously and nothing happens for a while. He then sinks into the charity shop sofa and watches snow for a few minutes, until it finally bursts into life. Then there's more demented button pressing, usually using the wrong bar.

This evening, he wanted to see something about armoured tanks, so, in we all traipsed, and the grizzly ritual started. I instantly selected the most comfortable duvet, watching the spectacle out of one eye; and, when it was obvious he was also asleep I relaxed as well. That's the part I don't quite understand, for we go in there, make ourselves comfortable, endure the rites and then go to sleep. Well, except for Wills for she loves it – particularly if there are animals involved. The moment the snow goes away she sits in front of it doing her 'Gramophone Dog' act. If it is only talking heads, she'll come and nap, checking now and again but if there are any animals she is hooked. The other night a running place was shown and she was transfixed, for it showed her what my past life had been like. A few weeks ago, it was a man who rescues Baby Jumpings, and she was besotted. So, as far as wild life programmes are concerned, oh it's heaven. Then he wakes up at some ungodly hour, puts the TV back to bed and out we all plod. Total waste of time, and I treat it with the contempt it deserves. Wills found the armoured tanks riveting.

Saturday

As the muse was so productive last Thursday, and as nothing happened out of the ordinary today, might as well finish telling you about our first days here.

He picked us up from the Rescue Centre, and bought us over the hill, and home. We got out of the car and had a little explor-atory wander around the garden. Then, he walked us around the perimeter and down to the stables. It was all very interesting, and we both explored, fit to burst. It was when we were near the orchard that I saw a small and Bobbing White Tail at the far end and, as one does, shot off – impervious to anything – with Willow trailing. Straight up the orchard, and the BWT dodged through a hole in the BWT fence into the oblong field, and I followed suit. BWT disappeared, but found myself amongst the horses. Now I know that Bertie had wanted to introduce us for he was scared at how I might react to them - Willow is well used to horses, as she has been around livery yards all her life. Well, I am also familiar with horses, for, in my previous life when foraging, it was horse feed that kept me alive all that time I was fending for myself.

Oh, I should explain how my experience of fending for myself began. One day, when returning from running, the back door of the van was opened and I was let out, for a comfort stop I assumed, as it was a long journey. However, they then drove off, having forgotten to re-load me. I was on my own in the great wide world for the first time ever. Not the faintest clue how to care for my needs, so then started a never ending quest to fill my stomach and find a comfortable place to sleep. Because I am no hunter, that was out so, I just got hungrier and hungrier. I tried all sorts of things like rotting road kill, noisome BWT, nettles and even horse droppings.

A few days later, by now ravenous, I found a horse with a feed bowl so tucked in and scoured the tail end of what it had left. Then found it was fed daily, and, for the next few days, horse feed became my means of survival; until the owner espied me and decided I was worrying his sheep, so got out his gun and chased me for three days. That was the low point and it was only by chance that a lady found me, popped me into her car and delivered me to the pound where I had my first decent meal for a week, + a comfortable bed, of course. Couple of days later, it was into a cage and the long journey to the Rescue Centre here. The rest you know.

Sorry about the diversion, and back to our first day here. I stood amongst the horses with no idea where I was, and taking no notice of them, for I had long ago learned that they are good for one thing - *cibus extremus*. Oh all right, emergency food! Heard him calling but it meant nothing for strangers are always calling me, so disregarded it. Finally, he came puffing up with Willow, who also took no notice of the nags, to the palpable relief of Bertie. So that was the start of curtailing our unrestricted freedom, for the orchard has now been cut off from us. I then found a hole under the gate and went exploring past the chichi offices and was deaf to his calls until I went up to be sociable with a nice lady who was passing. She held me while he, once again, puffed up to us.

By then he'd had enough of outside, so into the house we went. In the kitchen were the two beds. I immediately laid claim to mine, as one should. First rule of survival: always immediately establish your territory and where you'll be most comfortable. Tour continued, but one problem being that I'd never seen stairs before and he expected us to follow him up them. Willow, of course, bounded up and straight onto his bed looking like the cat that had got the cream. Not to be outdone, I stiffened the sinews and cautiously gave it a try.

At the top found there was another whole house. That was quite amazing. It also has low windows so you can see out; such a sensible idea. Then we had the problem of coming down again, and that I did not like so closed my eyes and *fell* down. That seemed to work because ended up on the floor downstairs. Then he rather let us both wander and get our bearings, and I had a great time sussing everything, but slightly blotted my copybook, for all the excitement meant I needed to do both, so I did - two in the dining room and one in the drawing room. Then I decided to test out the comfort of my bed while Wills set into the garden with relish, mainly the lawns. Enthusiastic but frustrated gardener it seems.

That was the first day in Willow's new and my first home. Over the next couple of days, my natural exploring instincts found a number of other imperfections in the fencing which would have been undetected except that when some well meaning person returned us, Willow would immediately make a beeline for the hole again. Because she is neither an original thinker nor a natural rebel, that would, of course, be her reaction – the pleasures of forbidden fruit. Whereas, having found and sussed the other side, I had no further use of the hole. Been there, done it, bought the T shirt.

CHAPTER 6

Wednesday

We returned to the lovely walk that Biddy had shown us, and, as we left through the trap in the butterfly field we met five smallish longhairs with long-ears who were very friendly. Happily latched onto them, and we carried on walking to the soon to be bluebell-infested woods. A vague feeling that all was not quite right flitted through my mind now and again. I couldn't quite put my finger on it; however the feeling soon passed when one of the longhairs pointed out something interesting. Finally through the heather, over the cricket pitch to the car. Then it hit me – we had lost Wills and himself. However he and Wills appeared from a totally different direction a little while later, though Bertie looked very thunderous.

He opened the tail gate, laid out the ramp for me and produced a handful of treats. The longhairs thought this wonderful, and shot up the ramp closely followed by Wills. They were then called down and Wills disobligingly followed. Well, treats were at stake here. General mayhem ensued trying to get her back without the longhairs while still trying to coax me up. Final solution was to allow Wills and the longhairs in, and lift me up, and then discard the longhairs one-by-one. It was like sardines when we were all in, so stood on my toes on the top of the bumper, getting in the way of the ejection. Someone was distinctly unamused, but the person attached to the longhairs fell about laughing.

As we got home Biddy was waiting for us and we were all very pleased to see each other with much mutual sniffing and tail wagging. Today, though, she wasn't with the Cheshire cat, but a crumpled man with a very long walking stick that reached as high as his head. The top divided into a "Y" in which he had his thumb, and his body hung down - rather like a monkey off a branch. I later found out it is actually called a 'thumb stick'. It was obviously very comfortable, and I assume he must live with Biddy and Cheshire. Well Thumbstick had a short waffle with Bertie - and then off they went, Thumbstick and Biddy I mean – to the post office, one assumes, for a couple of letters were clutched in the dangling hand.

Thursday

Perhaps it was a 'did usual things' day, except that in the evening we went to meet another of his friends. She is a distinguished lady who lives in a grand house. She was warmly welcoming and I could tell there was electricity between them. Now she has one of those black bouncing thieving jobbies and a tiny little bouncy. While I explored the vast pile felt faint unease that Willow would try her 'throw-it-in-the-air-and-land-dead' trick with the tiny little bouncy, but it was spunky, and snapped back, putting Wills in her place. She was obviously used to defending herself and, besides, this was her home territory. In fact, she and Wills quickly became friends while the BBT had not the slightest interest in either of us. Couldn't, for she was too busy defending her water and bed.

Curiosity satisfied, I spread out on the Aubusson carpet in front of the fire and dozed contentedly while he and the lady had supper, and talked and talked. Then, I felt the urge to pee, so got up and started to relieve myself against the wicker-work log basket, and that produced an explosive reaction from them both so I went into the kitchen and did it not once, but twice, for good measure. Distinguished was *not* amused. Somehow don't think we will be invited back for a long time. Actually we have subsequently welcomed Distinguished here but briefly.

Saturday

Now we had known that something was up, because all week the Housekeeper had been busier than usual and took ages in the dining room, always being careful to close the door afterwards. On Thursday, the Bookkeeper came, as she usually does, but instead of her normal paper shuffling and playing on her computer, spent all her time tidying up the office and putting her desk in the middle of the room where Housekeeper gave it a polish and then they both proceeded to lay it, and the dining room table, for lunch. All most unusual and faintly unsettling, so I took to my bed – safest place really. Willow was very excited and constantly tried to help.

Today all was revealed, for first off Housekeeper arrived – and she doesn't usually come on a Saturday. She appropriated the entire kitchen and utility room and bustled about with pans bubbling, constant crashing of the AGA doors and general mayhem. Then a steady stream of people started to arrive and we had our work cut out welcoming them. One big chap bought his small furry and, very like the tiny little bouncy I again feared for its safety, but it also managed to keep Willow at bay.

There were all sorts of interesting people, including: the Cheshire cat, Thumbstick the Game lady and Springy, although we'd not yet met each other socially. I rather fell for the wife of the chap who made the obelisk in the drawing room – which ruins an otherwise perfect mini-running track. She was LOUD, cheerful and she knew about woods too. Bertie was beside himself, rushing hither and thither, for it was a big party that filled both the sitting and drawing rooms.

I put great effort into amusing them and kept their attention at the start by giving all the human food on the low tables in the drawing and sitting rooms a detailed inspection to make sure Housekeeper had got them right. It helped too, when I licked the edge of the odd glass of alcohol. In the dining room and office there were no such props, so I gave the nose-height table in the corner a thorough going over, and as it held all the puddings and cheeses, my inspection tended towards the detailed. Didn't do anything too obvious of course, just the odd surreptitious sniff here, and lick there. I particularly liked the chocolate torte for it was dripping in alcohol, so my lick may have been a little overenthusiastic.

As a diversion a lovely woman with a strange accent kept feeding me titbits under the table. Now I can place her, for she tended to bore on to anyone who would listen about how and why she produced the two arty things that so clutter up our running area in the hall. The owner of the small furry also, for after lunch he took us all into the garden to show us the orange excrescence he made that sits on top of the wall.

There were a lot of them – people, not excrescences – and I thoroughly enjoyed the whole thing. It all overpowered Wills, so she retired to the sanctuary of her bed and when I tired I decided to lie down for a snooze with Bertie in plain view just in case he did anything naughty. Happily, that meant that virtually everyone had to step over me to get to the food. I don't think Willow likes hordes of people.

In due course the Great Art Lunch finished and we both had our work cut out waving goodbye. With some sadness, I hasten to add, for it had all been enormous fun. I don't think it will happen again for it took three days for the Housekeeper to get the place straight.

Sunday

Although he slept through the alarm clock again, the weather is improving so the walk was really rather nice. We went up the hill again to the big building. Hordes of people milling around everywhere and many were sitting on the benches by the big building eating their lunches. Nothing daunted I hopped over the stone wall – which is considerably higher than the car tailgate – and went up to socialise. Frantic calling from Bertie, for dogs are not allowed there except on a lead, but the immediate prospects were far too interesting to take any notice of him. To my surprise, most of them were quite resentful of my presence even though I worked the benches with charm, so was half relieved when he came and retrieved me.

Ever onwards and we then came across a load of active and excited dogs. As good hosts, after all, you can see home way down the valley from there, we entertained them and much fun was had. As there were three similar to me amongst the horde they knew how to run; I had a ball mixing with almost my own kind. He was quite patient and in due course they went their way and we went ours down the hill again until I latched onto a couple and their longhair long-ear as they walked back up to the big building, so sort of stuck with them. Now and again, Wills would turn up to try to get my attention. Finally the lady held me and he came puffing up to attach the lead. Then it dawned that they were not my today's handlers at all.

At the car he met a chum who was just starting his walk, and they talked while Wills sat, and I mooched. Oh, unlike Wills with her well padded bum, I don't do sitting. Wrong type of rear end so only option is either stand or lie – which is how we get our lazy reputation of course. Well at least that's my excuse. Wills sits for hours looking just like that little dog with the gramophone. She knows she looks 'cute' of course. My form of sitting is to lie like a Sphinx and that shows off my haunches beautifully. That position has another practical advantage for, barely moving a muscle I can roll onto my side and have a nap.

I have the same problem eating, for my legs are far longer than my neck; so it is practical to lie and eat with the dish held steady between my front paws, and, of course, I can roll on my side and have a nap between mouthfuls as well if needs be. Need does be quite often. Many seem to think that lying down to eat is strange but it was very fashionable for people to eat like that in days gone by.

Thursday

Today the Housekeeper took an unusual interest in the dining room once more, with furious polishing of the furniture, to be followed by delving into all the cupboards for the best china, as well as emptying the silver canteen. We tried to help, of course, but as much as I tidied the cutlery on the table she then re-arranged it. Wills didn't help of course, for she was too short to reach up. Have I mentioned that in the height department Wills is seriously wanting? I have, oh sorry. Ultimately we were banished and she, the Housekeeper I mean, went on messing behind closed doors. I suspect it can only mean one thing – a lunch.

Saturday

I was right, for Housekeeper arrived and started causing chaos in the kitchen as doors were flung open, draws left half closed, pots crashed and general mayhem reigned. It was particularly irritating because she constantly kept going to the fridge. Wills and I found this seriously annoying as we couldn't get to our nuts and water, which are kept in oblong bowls just under the fridge door and out of the way of any clumsy human feet that may be passing; have you noticed what clod hoppers they are?

Bertie, having given us each a cursory brush, then got into his smart clothes, and retired to the sitting room with the Saturday paper, the idle bugger.

The guests all arrived in one mad scrimmage – must have been waiting outside for the moment when we flung the gates open. We welcomed the BBT and LLH, + owners, + their baby, although I don't know why we bothered with the BBT, for she went straight in and up to the feed bin. She was foiled this time though, for he had thoughtlessly stuffed a rain coat into the bin, so she could get the lid off but no more. She then came into the kitchen and grabbed the two knotted rawhide chews he had bought us, climbed onto the thin bed and refused to give either up. She got very nasty, so we steered well clear and there she stayed throughout lunch only moving, with the tail end of the last chew, into the garden and then the car. The LLH on the other hand, had quite a bundle with Wills although she declined to run with me. She did feel a little overpowered by the pair of us, though, for we are both bigger than her.

I think it must have been a family get-together, for they were all much more effusive than normal and I noticed that the body language and tone of chat was both familiar and different. I particularly warmed to a pretty and petite woman in a little black Parisian number that flattered her figure. Not only did she make a great fuss of me but kept talking about our going to stay with them in their other house which was in wild and open country with only sheep covering the hillsides all around. I wonder if sheep can run. All those I've ever previously mixed with just stood and ate grass.

It was a lovely party, and became even more relaxed when the baby, which had been bawling its head off in the sitting room, joined them round the table. She was passed from hand to hand and little black number's eyes shone with excitement when she held her. Bertie was singularly uncomfortable and held it as he would a sack of feed. I know just how it felt, for he holds me like that too. We both warmed to the older lady, for she always seemed to have something tasty in her hand which, somehow, slipped into our mouths when he wasn't looking.

Eventually the time came to leave so we fussed each into their cars, the little black number taking a gash table that had been cluttering up the office, and they parted in the same mad scramble. We closed the gate, and finally had our lunch. There was fallout, for the BBT and LLH were given the rest of the pack of the rawhide chews for neither of us had liked them one bit. Good riddance.

Then there followed a pretty uneventful 'did usual things' sort of a week with Bertie at home quite a lot. Oh, the Excrescence man paid a visit and they went down to the barn then came back to the terrace with measuring tapes. Now I wonder what *that* could mean.

CHAPTER 7

Saturday

He was being his normal lazy self and doing precious little up to lunch time – well the post bought a shoal of letters which seemed to necessitate a lot of calculating on the computer, which took AN AGE, and then he demolished the newspaper. It was a lovely sunny day and quite mild, by far the best day for the past few months, and he did have the grace to leave the back door open. Yes, it was that mild.

Finally, at lunch time he left us, and went shopping. Well no convenient bog rolls – he's finally learned that one – so I had a root around on the unit where all our 'stuff' is kept, you know: treats, dental sticks, chews and tins. It is all supposed to be beyond investigation height but when he's not there, I stretch up on my back legs and that extends my reach by a couple of feet. I can also pull out the tin recycling bin slightly to use as a step which extends the range even further. I'm canny enough <u>never</u> to do either when he's around though.

Out of boredom had a quick mosey and the only thing portable was a small bottle of my anti-inflammatory pills with a tamper-proof cap that I could just reach. About enough for a month and I know it cost a fortune. Hauled that down and took it to bed where I managed to chew the bottle open and then happily demolished the entire contents for they really are very nice. Boy did he hit the roof when he returned; and nothing could be done for my second home was closed for the weekend. Tip: try to do things like this on a Saturday afternoon for it causes maximum angst. It did nothing for my gammy leg though, for I am still doing my Long John Silver act.

Well he had been thinking of us when shopping for he returned with a little red ball which Wills instantly collared and kept in her mouth for the rest of the day. Every time she dropped it and I went to investigate, it was snarl, snap and into her mouth again. She's learned to do that from the Bouncy Black Thief. There was a blue one, too, but it held no interest for either of us. A squeaky one also seemed to materialise but as I don't know about toys, took not a blind bit of notice. Anyway Wills purloined it and became very emotional when I investigated, which is no bother for I am not materialistic. Little things little minds.

Oddly neither of us ever tested the squeak, but it ended up in my bed and kept waking us when I turned over. Willow does seem to need the occasional bit of quality time, for she had spent most of the morning on her own out of sight doing whatever she does. I'll be out soaking up the sun and when he appears to check on us I can belt back to him with a great grin and that leads to some enjoyable 'together' time without old Me Too horning in for attention.

He was so lazy that even though it was the PERFECT day for a walk, none was forthcoming for he then went upstairs. We had a very pleasant hours sleep together. When I say 'together' that's not strictly accurate for he's in bed and I'm on the floor where I can see his every move. Did try the bed once, but as both of us are bony, and have wriggly bums, neither one slept a wink. It was not a success. Wills retired to I don't know where and good job too for she has become, have I mentioned it, very tetchy recently.

Later it was down to muck-out; all rather last minute before the Livery person came to bring the horses in, so I tried to help him. Independent bugger insisted on doing it on his own, though, so I tested out the clean bed instead. Then the *dénouement* for Wills and I had a massive burn-up.

Now that must be the understatement of the decade, for it was the ultimate, the supreme, the total summation of a run. As we bought the horses in, I had an unscheduled and unusually liquid #2 for I felt a run welling up and I then walked Livery lady back up the drive and through the gate – one does have certain standards – while Wills watched from the stables. I turned and started walking purposefully back, you know the sort of thing: head down and shoulders hunched. Happily Wills took the hint for she went down on her front legs, and I saw her tail start to wag menacingly as a challenge.

Then we broke - up the mound to the bird bath lawn, through the rose bower, around the front, through the Straits of Magellan, onto the lawn by the orchard and round to the big lawn. Sliding 360 degree turn and back through Magellan onto the front lawn, round Cape Horn, onto the bird bath lawn, onto the mound, over the sleeper bank. Then it was over the drive and around the big lawn. All at full speed and the possible permutations were endless for one variation was through the Straits of Hormuz onto the terrace and up the steps back onto the big lawn. Or another was to approach Hormuz from the other side clipping the edge of the terrace in one mighty leap. My body was at full stretch ditto my brain doing lightning calculations, and now and again Willow added her variants. We were possessed.

All the while Bertie stood on bird bath watching, and I could feel his soul running with us. Most of the time I'd be leading, but often Wills took over. It was the run of my life; far better and longer than anything I'd ever experienced in my professional days because we were doing it through sheer *joie de vivre* and with such endless variety. We were transported, ecstatic and supreme in that rare world known to so few.

I'll say this. Have had to re-assess my thinking about Willow's family background, for no one but another speed hound could have lasted so long at such velocities. It was the ultimate, the single minded consummation of 3,000 years of my past. It was our obeisance to the altar of the definitive godhead SPEED.

We finally finished by peeling apart and zooming onto the bird bath lawn from opposite ends of the garden and doing synchronised hand brake turns to end up either side of Bertie. We only needed coloured smoke to complete the picture. Now, when we have had lesser burn-ups he usually bends down and gives us each a stroke; but today that was superfluous and the three of us just walked contentedly, line abreast, back through Hormuz to the terrace.

Wills was so fired up that she broke away and zinged down the terrace and back, jumping up into his arms like a lap dog. Sent him flying of course – well 25 kilos hitting you in the chest would. As he lay on the lichen-covered paving we indulged in our first ever threesome bundle. Great fun, but did nothing for my gammy leg for I've been barely able to walk since.

Don't think Housekeeper is going to be impressed for his anorak is a mess with one enormous tear in the arm, and she and sewing needles are strangers. All night I dreamed about The Great Run, re-living the adrenalin fuelled experience.

So The Great Run ended.

Sunday

Now we knew there would be no walk today for the Nephew came with Slobber Chops, and they had just been on a walk. We were very happy to see the mutt. I know he can't run but he's a friendly enough fellow and, besides, he's part of the family. The balls were still here then and he added to the throng with a chew proof one that Wills rather took to but they all sort of went after that. They had to go, for Willow became impossible every time I tried to investigate one; it was snap and snarl, and even when he picked one up and put it between my paws, she gave a sly and evil look while she surreptitiously sneaked it back.

After a lot of the usual chat, we finally saw them into their car, and as we did the usual courtesy of walking down and opening the gate, we espied a white bobbing tail in the BWT field. Instantly we clicked into auto pilot and were off. Could vaguely hear him calling and whistling but the BWT, plus all the others we'd disturbed, were our sole goal. Roamed happily up and down the barbed wire fence both quite oblivious to him until Wills came through the ether and reluctantly returned. I was still impervious and chasing and when one went through the barbed wire, so did I. After quite a while, got bored negotiating the bulrushes in the swamp and came back into the BWT field by which time Wills and him were right beside me.

Would I follow them home? I would not! Then followed a most unpleasant and undignified walk home with him pulling my collar until it slipped over my head. That was followed by him walking me between his legs holding my chest, then pushing my bum, and, finally, the ultimate indignity: lifting my back legs and walking me as if pushing a wheel barrow. If I hadn't still been in such a euphoric state, I'd have protested very forcibly.

I managed to get a small nick on the ear wound plus a useful gash on one hind leg; BUT I did a real humdinger on my good front leg. Home and he wiped it all down. Then a piece of Gamgee to hold the large flap of skin in place bound on with sticky tape. I yelled fit to burst as the sticky was applied. Not because I could actually feel anything, but just in case you know. I was hyped and I shivered with shock for a good half hour afterwards

Bertie is bound to finally cut off the BWT field. That'll take some time, one assumes, but these traumas just cannot continue, for it's so enervating afterwards. Then we had lunch which I really couldn't face, and to bed for a thorough clean up and welldeserved sleep. Willow's bed of course, for I have tended to appropriate that as my day bed recently.

I've felt poorly ever since, so no playing with Wills at mucking-out time, or bringing the horses in, and in fact, all I've wanted to do is sleep it off.

Bertie did eventually cut off the BWT field for he'd been meaning to do it from the second day we were here. His inexcusable laziness has caused me a couple of very nasty weekends. He took forever, of course. Have I mentioned that he's not the most practical person? It all looks rather untidy and Heath Robinson but it is effective for he challenged us to get into the BWT field and we couldn't. We are now trussed up behind security that makes Dartmoor Prison seem like a 'walk-in' detention centre.

Mind you, the BWT field is not entirely out of bounds for Wills once found a way into it from the triangle field, but as we can never go in there except under supervision..... That BWT field is turning into our Holy Grail methinks, for it reawakens all our primal hunting instincts.

About slipping out of the collar so easily. I suppose I should explain that I have a long head that is elegant and streamlined; and it is held by my powerful neck, which is nearly the same circumference. Unlike Willow, whose ears 'talk', mine are useless flaps of uncontrollable floppy skin that fold into my neck like a swing wing fighter when I run; so wearing collars that don't come off is a non-starter. If my current collar were any tighter it would throttle me. Not being dogs, or only knowing about doggy-dogs, humans didn't think of that when they made the laws. It proves the old saw that "the law is a-ass, a-idiot"*.

*'*Oliver Twist*' Charles Dickens

Monday

I really did not want to get up this morning. I rather suspect the anti-inflammatory pills on that score for could hardly drag myself out of bed and, sort of, made a show for the walk; but no toilets and no running. Put in an appearance when the horses went out and then back to bed. In due course he bundled me into a different car from normal – rather comfortable, actually, for I lay along the back seat with a good view out as he drove very fast to the big town with the X-ray machine.

Sure enough that was our destination and I revelled in lying on the mat in the reception area once again; there is something about it that is very comfortable. Then I had a sniff at a small and very furry in a cage that spat, accompanied by thunderous shouts from the owner. He left me and it was into the familiar warm room of cages, mine being particularly roomy and comfortable on the ground floor but with a seriously low ceiling.

They then dressed my gash and did a similar dressing but in a nicer colour on the other leg, and out of it spouted a plastic tube just as I had following my op. I really did feel very ill, but the food was nice, if Spartan, and I could sleep my heart away.

We'll draw a veil over the next five days and, truth to tell, it was all such a blur of tubes, handling by kindly strangers and constant activity all around while I longed for the peace of home, so cannot say that I remembered much of it except that I felt very mouldy and slept and slept. Whenever a tan dog came in I did rouse myself thinking it may be Wills, but it never was.

He came and visited me quite often and even bought Wills once. I was very pleased to see familiar faces although while I could manage a smile and winding myself around both of them it didn't extend to any tail activity. On Thursday I saw the Morpheus needle and sure enough out I went like a light and woke to find that they had mended the gashes in both my front and back legs which had been so irritating.

The next day they changed the dressing, and he came to collect me. We went home in the nice different car so I could lie contentedly and watched the world pass by. Only fell off the seat twice. When I arrived home, the first thing I did, after a curt greeting to Wills, was test my 'who's been sleeping in my bed?' for it smelt of her. She must have missed me as much as I did her.

The concern that everyone at the X-ray place exhibited suggests that this has been something of a close call.

Sunday

The past couple of days have proved quite a bind. When we arrived home on Friday I realised just how Spartan the menu had been at the X-ray place for I was ravenous and ate and ate. Then found he was not letting me out, except on a lead. Wills very put out for she wanted to play and I wanted to stretch my legs in the usual way. It also seriously hampered my normal toilet arrangements where I sniff and wander endlessly. Think about it, then don't think about it, or, because it is too cold, or, sniff for the right spot with intent until something interesting distracts me, or, he has lost patience, or, I've forgotten why we are out and finally we come back into the warmth of the house. After all, there is always the utility room in extremis.

All this inactivity made me take the route of the terminally bored and I'm snacking incessantly while licking the dressing even when told NO but it was never a very loud NO so I take NO notice; well a bit of notice but not much. It's a sound policy to humour the provider of one's provender.

Yesterday we went back to the emporium to have my dressing changed. Had to negotiate the hated road and I put on a good show of reluctance both going in and coming out again. Naturally had to be lifted in and out the car which is feeling much better since it has been away. All those noisy knockings when we go over a bump seem to have gone away. It was the nice Scottish man again and because I know he won't hurt me, while on my guard, I forbore to cry.

Then it was home. Have I mentioned the Siberian wind we are having from the East? Well we are and the house is like an icicle when the heating is off. Even with the AGA heaving away gallantly in the kitchen we are frozen. There is one draught that he had not been able to isolate. So, a rather determined look materialised, and then started the 'sucked-finger-in-the-air' routine. He went out of the kitchen and down the passage. Well after an age he did locate something around the coat cupboard door, so big white rolls of sealing strips appeared. He set to work around the door, finally finishing by purloining a fancy needlework door stop from the sealed front door.

Did it cure the draught? Well, let's be kind and say the kitchen's no longer a deep freeze, more a Tepidarium because there is still one nasty little icicle squirting in at floor height. I took no notice of his puny efforts and polished off the nuts instead. Then I felt that I just had to thank him for his efforts there, puny as they were; so I went and tangled myself around his legs in gratitude and he bent down and hugged me. I felt most content purring quietly, and sensed that the same went for him. Perhaps we are both turning into people who do have 'owners' after all. Then Me Too horned in and spoiled the moment.

CHAPTER 8

Saturday

I am sure that I have made it very plain from the very start, that I find jumping up into the back of a car rather demeaning; as befits my status, I should be LIFTED in. Wills, by the way has long become a scab on this issue and she has definitely gone over to the dark side.

Well all this lifting is hurting his back, so he's resorted to calling in the dog trainer. I'm sure I have mentioned her before. Well, to-day this jolly lady with a fruity and laughing voice turned up. She and Bertie appeared to be good friends; AND she smelt of dogs.

So, it was on with my walking collar and the smart leather lead. The boot door was opened and she put a bale of straw down. Then she produced some scrummy bits of cooked bacon from her pocket; but I could only have them if I jumped onto or off the bale and into or out of the car. It was a great game until I noticed that the helpful bale started sliding off to the side, necessitating some increasingly fancy footwork.

Finally, it went and we were back to square one. The bacon may have been nice but not *that* nice. So she then produced a ramp and more of the bacon bribes. Well, front legs OK, but my back ones would not co-operate and kept falling off the sides of the ramp. Back end must be a bit spastic for I've always had trouble handling it and occasionally it definitely has a mind of its own. Not a problem running of course, for the power is all on the shoulders, spine and rump. Willow, of course, had no such inhibitions and constantly ran up and down and even, occasionally, cut out the middle man and jumped, but then, as you know, her mind is ruled by her stomach.

Eventually got the hang of it and the jolly lady went her merry way with, of course, the tail end of the bacon. Those, she gave to her mutt, who had ridden shot gun for the bale, in the back of her very large car. Now what did it, the mutt I mean, do to deserve the bacon?

Consequently every time the car is involved, out the ramp comes. I usually disdain it; however, just occasionally, I do condescend – particularly as he now has treats on hand – although there is the invariable problem with the back pins for they still have minds of their own and slip off. Suppose that like St. Augustine I'll have to succumb one day but, not yet.

Monday

As it was supposed to be the X-ray place today, he took a day off work. They seem to have mended me so well that the dressing was left off and I feel much happier for that. Unfortunately, we have reverted to those dreadful pills they gave me last time but when he gives me one it is always followed by a little something nice, so all complaints tend towards the sotto voce.

It has been a very cold day with an icy east wind and we have remained tucked up beside the AGA mostly sleeping, except when I felt very frisky and tried to get Willow into a bundle in the dining room. That stopped as soon as it started, though, as my wounded leg gave me a nasty warning twinge. Held it up for sympathy and got none.

Outside it smells ominously like more snow and that would warm everything up again. It tried very hard last night but there was only that mean dusting that does nothing for the temperature but freezes everything so I suspect he'll be carting water from the house down to the stables all day.

At about lunch-time, Arty lady came and they went off with much excited chatter about 'well as they're booked until whenever shall we do....?' Actually they didn't DO anything but went out for one l-o-n-g lunch instead, leaving us behind.

Decided to fill in the time by rearranging my bed, for bog rolls are becoming rather de trop. Have you noticed that when some-thing new and fascinating comes along the first time it is very exciting but as it gets repeated so the lustre tarnishes (except sex of course but even that's now rather *yesterday* since my op),until it finally goes the way of all flesh. Wills' gardening enthusiasm has waned considerably recently, too, you know.

I also registered my disapproval by leaving a large wet patch around the rubber mat by the back door, then the dining room, then the sitting room, then the drawing room and just for good measure two massive #2's in the dining room. It also seems that walks are out for he has made no attempts on that score. Perhaps he is just being lazy again, or he doesn't like the cold, but either way we are being deprived. I'm very inclined to register a complaint. Now I wonder if it's the Rescue Centre to whom I should write.

When I was being collected from the X-ray place, they kept remarking on how much I slept. He had to explain that all greyhounds have this great affinity to their pits. Apart from running, it is the ONLY thing in our lives, and everything else is secondary. To me, Nirvana would be the ability to sleep 23½ hours a day. Some chance of that ever happening here.

Tuesday

Now I know what multi-tasking is, as we had a demonstration this evening. So far as I can make out it is a very good way to get into a thorough mess and do a number of jobs very badly. Bertie sat down to have his supper while trying to print out this manuscript for us to take to the lovely wheelchair lady across the road; but the printer ran out of ink half way through, so he messed about delving into its innards, changed the cartridge and then printing things which had then to be reprinted. Finally, he set it off again and it was left to itself leaving mountains of wasted paper which the skinflint abhors.

He came back happily to his, by now congealed supper, having totally forgotten that he had some tapioca in the top of the top oven when we all know it should be in the bottom of the bottom oven on a baking tray. Naturally, it boiled over and has stained the floor of the oven. Meanwhile the pea soup he was also making for his midnight snacks burnt dry and the peas are now a solid and useless black lump, with the pot equally black. Their stink adding to the noisome smells with which we are already assailed from the caked-on tapioca. He was taking a short cut, of course, and cooking them in a pan on the hot plate, when they should have been in a casserole dish in the bottom oven, simmering gently. End result – no tapioca, no pea soup and he unnecessarily wasted a load of paper while gulping down a cold supper as he manfully juggled the disasters.

The final insult was that half way through it Wills asked to go out and he took no notice; so she followed my example and went in the utility room instead. He was <u>furious</u> but whose fault was that? I told you, Bertie's a moron, well meaning and kindly but a moron just the same; and the practical Housekeeper will froth at the mouth tomorrow. I suppose that means the wire brush for the oven, which so sets my teeth on edge.

Wednesday

I was so right, for the first thing the Housekeeper did was hoist the wire brush out of its hiding place, opened both doors and attacked the oven, squeaking away as she banished the baked tapioca. It was so dreadful, like a nail scraping over a slate, that I just had to move out; so consoled myself on one of the sitting room duvets until he came home from work. I did manage to sneak an empty packet of cornflakes through as well and set about tasting the wax bag inside. It was 'different', but the cardboard was not to my liking.

When he eventually came home, I made a great show of having missed him by winding in and out of his legs. Wills jumped up and down wagging her tail frantically and trying to lick his nose, just in case he'd take us for a walk. It worked too, for after lunch we did just that. Not a very long one, for it was bitter, but it was a walk all the same, and did clear the cobwebs. I think that he feels the cold as badly as me because he slows right down to a crawl – perhaps the endless fags contribute.

Oh dear! I think that I may be turning into a doggy-dog. You see, whenever he lets us out for specific reasons (usually after I've had a bit of a tuck-in + drink) we walk to the top of the terrace steps, and he starts his Witch Doctor chant of 'wee wee Willie Wills, pee pee Bandit Boy'. Now I know that means don't go running off or, indeed, having a bundle, but does mean attending to our ablutions. Well, I notice that of late that I have started to sniff around meaningfully and then finally pee and sometimes crap as well. Old age you know or it could be because she gets a regular supply of a treat when we come in whereas often I don't. But I do if there has been a leg lift and pregnant pause. Sometimes, just to fox him I fake it. Still no walks though and that is getting beyond a joke.

Thursday

And someone must have had a word, for he came home from work, gave us our lunch had a cup of coffee and the inevitable coffin stick, then it was on with smart collars – of which Wills always gets so over excited that he has real difficulty putting it on – while I just stand patiently expecting the attention. You'll have guessed by now that I am a phlegmatic sort. I don't strive for anything but just accept things as they come or subtly arrange that they do come. Then out to the car. Out came the ramp.

Oh, I should explain that I've virtually given up on that one as well for all it does is delay us going so it tends to be tokenism rather than sedition. I really am turning into a doggy-dog after all.

Then it was out to the cricket pitch and, as it turned out, our favourite short walk through the butterfly field and back over the heath. We hadn't been walking long before I espied three greyhounds on a converging path so I went over to make my mark. Seems we had all been in the profession, but I never ran against them for they ran in this country while I ran over the water. One was on a lead and I heard her lady say that if she were let off, she'd be gone. Looking at her cracking legs, I certainly can believe it. Those legs were made for running VERY FAST.

Ever onwards and when we got to the stile trap I went through with no resistance. Well, once again, I've found that it is useless kicking up a fuss for I'll be got through it somehow, come hell or high water, and so may as well give in with some dignity. Mind you, it should be noted that he doesn't go through it but takes the easy option of climbing over the stile. Something about sauce for the goose methinks.

We'd just arrived in the butterfly field when I came across a strong scent of a BWT which got me going through the dead bracken and brambles. I could hear him calling weakly, but this was serious stuff so ignored him. Bertie and Wills came back and stood by the bracken. I heard him bawling my name, but I just looked blankly at him for didn't know who he was or why he was making such a noise. Beyond him, I espied two very large blacks with long hair that looked as if they had had a bad day under the hair dryer for it all stood straight out like a dandelion. Just had to say 'hullo,' and they were very friendly. However their owner was in a bit of a hurry – testing out his smart new running shoes no doubt – so they went their way and we continued down the field.

After this I decided to stay very close to Bertie just to give him re-assurance for he can be very vague at times and occasionally needs reminding of where we are.

The walk may have been short, but it was fun, and we came home to the inevitable mucking-out. Well I helped him a bit, but mainly entertained Willow insofar as my gammy leg allowed, so she didn't get in his way. Came in feeling much happier on a job well done and after the dental stick, gave my bed a trial run again. Couldn't even be bothered to go and help bringing in the horses. Now here is a strange thing – for both the greyhounds and the hair dryers came from beyond the snarling traffic town – so it is lovely that we can share our home ground with visitors.

Friday

As usual, the morning started with his frantic rushing around but today he looked quite particularly smart. Loaded us into the car – and I used the ramp again - and off we went to the very big town over the hill with the snarling traffic. There we went to this enormous hospital and he left us in the car, while it swallowed him up. Well, car parks are pretty boring so I slept while Wills looked at all the passing humanity.

He was gone a fair while and we came home but via the jolly Wheel Chair lady over the road, where he had a cup of coffee, I had a love in with her, and Wills went to the kitchen to see what she could scrounge off the carers. Quite a lot, I think. We were delivering the first draft manuscript of this diary so far, for she knows us pretty well now.

You see, when we first came he took us to meet Wheel Chair and we liked it all very much, for the house is full of laughter all the time and is warm and comfortable with a large fire blazing away, and interesting rooms to investigate. She has a commendably comfortable carpet. It's the sort of place which feels like a loving home, so you want to be on your best behaviour. Well, one needs to lay down markers just in case.

She has two helpers, and we quickly found that because they were not dog-savvy, we were fed endless titbits. Her house overlooks the oblong field and every morning when we go out he waves to her bedroom window even though we can't see *her* but she can see *us* from her bed. I suppose you could say that although the horrid road is all that separates us, Wheel Chair is our next door neighbour, not counting the six cottages on the farm, or the Duchess, or the people from across the way behind the high laurel hedge who we don't know. She's a jolly nice neighbour to have too.

In the afternoon he was off doing his Friday moonlighting again. Bit of a conscience there, for he hasn't managed it for the past three weeks. Obviously no walks flying our way, but that's par for the course, and to be expected. As he'd left the door open to the rest of the house, registered my disapproval in the usual way, but this time did such a neat job of it he didn't notice for quite a while. My selected victim was the sitting room door pillar which I managed to hit square on so it all ran down and through the crack between the carpet and the pillar. 'Nice shooting' I thought and virtually undetectable.

Anyway, when we were let out for our last you know what, WITH the flashing collars, I had a mini burn-up and in executing a tight turn did my leg in again and could barely walk back to the house. One would have thought that after resting it for so many days it would have lasted a bit longer. Perhaps it just became weak from so little exercise and I am now overdoing it on that front. It's not me but Wills who suffers of course for she gets no exercise. Oh well.

Saturday

Now something must have got into him, or perhaps it was the fact that it turned out to be a lovely sunny day, if a little on the chill side, but when he arrived home from shopping it was lunch and almost immediately on with our walking collars and leads. Then down to the front gate with me sliding on my arse in protest even to bumping down the front steps bump-bump-bump like Pooh Bear to the awful road. Once there, he obviously needed reassurance for he held the lead very short and I mean *almost throttling me* short. I'd never realised that he was quite so terrified of it, the road I mean. So, I put on my brave face and strode out manfully, protecting them both, but I did feel a *little* scared of the cars. Besides that, my bad leg from last night was giving me gyp.

Then, when the road was silent – it's a sharp corner by the lane we turn onto so we cannot see the cars coming either way – we crossed the road and he let us off up the lane to do Biddy's lovely walk through the open fields and working coppice. Freedom at last, and we both went exploring. A car came but I was deaf to his call but it soon turned into one of the drives; as luck would have it, the one in which I'd taken refuge. The sun shone, the grass crackled with growth and it was just lovely as we gently explored. I didn't stray too far, for my leg was still rather hurting, and, besides, I liked the companionship. Down through the coppice, along the secret walk through the beech wood, up to Biddy's house; when on went the leads again for the dire road. I did try a diversion by ducking into a handy cottage garage, but to no avail. Once home, he let us off and we went out to play, for poor Willow had so much energy. Mind you the 'playing' was her rushing around, mainly mining, while I lay on the mound soaking up the weak sun.

In the evening, Bertie fired up the TV as there was something he plainly wanted to watch very badly but it was just at the same time as our last out for the day; so he delayed a short while, then switched on the terrace light and let us out – by then we were both bursting so there was no hanging around. I even beat Wills to the draw and came to join him on the terrace while we waited for her to finish, for like all wimmin she can sometimes take an unconscionable time. What do they get up to?

Perhaps I should explain that on the terrace we have a 'feature'. It is a dinky Art Nouveau bird bath which isn't used as one at all so has a number of ironstone rocks in it, arranged artfully of course (we are on ironstone). When it rains the bird bath fills and the ironstone taints the water which becomes a novel and very nice drink so I always indulge myself for it is at a comfortable height. Happily Willow is too short. Have I? Yes I have.

Well, while we waited for Wills I wandered over and took a sniff of the bird bath, and what assailed me was not the scented water, but a faint something far more exciting, although some way off beyond the low terrace wall. Wandered over and sniffed under one of the bushes in the bed the other side of the wall and the more I sniffed the stronger and more exciting the smell. It was unmistakably a BWT and under the bush too. Now I was really fired up and my tail went nineteen to the dozen as I riffled into the bush, but as the wall got in the way, hopped over it and attacked the bush from that side. Deeper and deeper I went into the bush, until all that was exposed was my bum and furiously wagging tail. No good that way so went around to the other side, then the middle, then the first side and this time managed to push right through the bush to the other side. Wills came bursting back from whatever had kept her and instantly joined the fray. Then, when I had withdrawn to regroup, I heard him calling, so acknowledged him over the top of the bush and started my next assault. Next thing was the nuclear option as I felt the lead being attached to my collar. The chase was over for it is never any good resisting the lead.

In we went and back to the TV, where I settled myself on one of the duvets for it was plain that trouble was brewing. Sadly, Wills is not so prescient and walked around constantly making her 'I need to go out' whine, then sitting and looking at him with pleading eyes. Up, down, up, down, scampering to the back door, and generally making a great fuss. Obviously it broke his concentration so the TV was put out of its misery and the doors of the cabinet slammed shut with an ill-tempered bang and he stormed off to the kitchen and the bloody computer.

His mood was obvious, so I kept a very low profile and crept quietly into my bed. No point in rocking the boat. Wills, on the other hand carried on relentlessly and then, boy did she get it.

WILLOW BED! She instantly obeyed, but sat looking pleadingly at him rather than lie down. After a while she started whimpering again and this time it was a terse **BED!** Finally she got the message and lay down. Not before time either. As I told you, she can be very insensitive at times and she had been disturbing my sleep. Humans are moody creatures and do need to be humoured, and that's a lesson she has never learned.

I will say this for Bertie. We never go to bed with any bad feelings, for no matter what's happened during the day, as he starts for his bed he patches things up by quietly stroking us in our beds which we really love, for he is saying 'all is right with the world, and sleep well', so we lie very still, shut our eyes contentedly as he gently strokes, and do just that.

CHAPTER 9

Sunday

You know my attitude to the TV. Well, tonight it was rather reversed, for we went through the dreadful machinations to bring it alive again and, as usual, I retired to the not so comfortable duvet for the Housekeeper had decided to cut out the surrounding draughts with a sort of cardboard box surround, only it got in the way of trying to get comfortable. Thankfully, after much harrumphing from me for the second night running, he finally saw the awkwardness and took it away; and I moved to the other duvet which is too small for me. Well, it appears that there was some sort of car programme for him to watch, and we settled down.

By 'we' I mean I settled down for a snooze, while Wills went to bed in disgust because there were no animals; so only he actually watched. Now a bit more of an explanation about our domestic set up would be useful. The TV is on a cabinet with doors, and all the flashing boxes are in the cabinet with quite a space between them and the top. If we want to be posh we can close the doors but when being untidy (which is all the time), they stay open. It is partially filled with DVDs and tapes but there is still a fair old hole there.

Well, after a while I heard my squeaky ball. Naturally I went over to investigate. Just could not find it anywhere but could hear it constantly squeaking away from around the cabinet area. Stood there investigating inside, around, behind the cabinet, then looking at the TV for a goodly while, but found it all most confusing, so wandered out to the kitchen for a snack – my motto being 'when in doubt have a bite'. While I was eating, there was squeaky, on my bed, so brought it back into the sitting room where I could keep an eye on it. Now it was with me, it stopped squeaking in the TV cabinet. That shows it knows on which side its bread is buttered.

Monday

I don't quite know what has come over Bertie, for after getting home from work, instead of his usual cup of strong coffee and a cigarette while he delved into the computer as we wolfed down our lunch – an agreeable change of pilchards in tomato sauce today – and as soon as we were finished it was on with leather collars, out to the car and up to the car park which meant a welcome walk up (or around) the hill with the big building at the top. It happened that he decided we should go around, thank goodness, for I cannot stand seeing him struggle so hard trying to breast the last steep bit to the big building. It was a quite lovely mild day, for the horrid east wind has gone to wherever winds go, and left the sun shining fit to burst. It was lovely and we skipped around – well as much as my leg would allow – chasing any number of dead ends.

Then we came across a VERY well groomed Black Long Crinkly Tufted Hair for it only came out in places like her knees and the top of her head – oh and the very end of her tail. She smelt dreadful and wore a lurid pink coat with matching pink bootees and both her collar and lead were also pink. They all, lead included, had sparkling shinies sewn on. Her owner, while wearing the most inappropriate shoes for sand and mud – even I noticed them – proved to be very friendly, although she didn't smell of dog.

Bertie, who cannot resist a skirt, had a long chat with her as you do when walking together, and found out that she comes from a very very large town, and this was their weekly slug of fresh country air. Well, we all fell in for the rest of the walk and the BLCTH walked, on the lead, just as Wills used to do. She walked straight ahead looking neither to right nor left. She reacted to nothing and was impervious to any nice smells that needed investigating. What is worse, she took no notice of what we were doing and that is very non-doggy. I pondered this for quite a while, and finally came to the conclusion that all her normal walks must be on pavements with a dog walker in a hurry for, apparently, this is the only time she is with her owner. When we arrived at our cars she dutifully jumped up into A CAGE in the back of theirs. Although she obviously lives in sophisticated luxury, I felt sorry for her. I think I prefer our slap-dash set up thank you.

Tuesday

This morning when he came down I felt very like the model that would not get out of bed for less than $10,000 a day. Only what would I do with money? So I dragged myself up very reluctantly. Anyway it was such a brisk morning that feeding the horses and then doing the apology for first walk of the day managed to fire me up enough to indulge in a bit of rough play with Wills as we came over the big lawn. I was all for carrying on inside but, somehow, we have rather stopped playing in the house for all these arty things so get in the way, besides he tends towards the gentle perambulation inside, so we rather follow suit.

Foiled on that front, I decided to play with the squeaky ball for a while, which was fairly short term quite honestly. So felt that there must be a better use for my time and went back to bed instead.

I should elaborate on this 'NO' thing and Willow. That is the only admonition we ever have (barring the occasional 'BED' when Wills is restless) but it ranges from a quiet 'nooooughu' through to the mighty thunder in intensity. If it is 'nooooughu', that can be noted, but safely ignored. If followed by the rather more intense 'Nooooh' a slight pause, and a look of 'what, me?' will be sufficient, but after that, the ice becomes steadily thinner. When storm warnings have been hoisted, I invariably stop altogether, but this is where Wills is so stupid, for she persists. So with her it is almost invariably the full bolt of lightning. Mind you as she isn't a rebel, disgustingly conformist actually, any form of admonition is a fairly rare occurrence but when it does happen....WATCH OUT....

I also should explain that when switched into chase mode, nothing else exists and when the hunt is over it normally takes a fair while for the mist to lift. During that time, I am like a zombie in every way: impervious to calls, whistles or even contact and can only stand shaking gently, unable to respond to any stimulus for my brain has gone into limbo. Only when it has all finally cleared, do I recognise my surroundings, and any scratches or wounds start to bother me; and this can take anything up to an hour.

Wednesday

It may seem that I am unnecessarily obsessed by walks, but it is not so, for I am quite happy to give them a miss, and they do interrupt my power naps. It's Bertie who is obsessed. I think it may be because his work is sedentary and as he does precious little around here that's how he gets any exercise. It may also have a lot to do with Wills shedding some fat, and I must say that she has recently started looking slimmer and it suits her. Unfortunately, it has also made her far more energetic and sometimes she is impossible, particularly when my leg is playing up.

Anyway, today it was to be the lovely Biddy walk through the car parts and working coppice. We had barely started to negotiate the awful road into the lane before there was a shout behind us. We turned to see a spare and springy man with not one, but two tiny whites with Bristling Short Hairs – one with a great tail that curved up into the sky, but the other seems to have lost his, for it is a mere stump. How can one steer and employ air brakes with a stump? Still, he does seem to manage, but then they aren't exactly high speed merchants. They were peas in a pod and great fun to be with for they are also hunters but more of the nose variety than us. They also had what I thought were gammy legs for they tended to run about with one back leg retracted, until I noticed that it was only now and again when they came across a particularly interesting scent.

Perhaps I should also explain that when we come to the end of the walk and leave the secret beech wood, we then go through the gardens of two pretty cottages. Nice and very neat gardens with big lawns and a large lake beyond. As I'd never seen anyone around I assumed the houses were empty, but today it turned out that they belong to the Bristling Short Hairs, for one peeled off to the first cottage, and the other followed Springy man into the second.

Anyway, it appears that Springy and Bertie are good friends, so we all fell in together rather like the pilgrims in *The Canterbury Tales* and wended our way around the walk; by a strange co-incidence, some of it on the original Pilgrims Way walked by Geoffrey Chaucer. It was certainly great fun as the BSH proved to be enormously curious about everything and full of life. It did help that the sun was also shining through the beech trees and sparkling off the winding river far below us. That's the river that goes past the BWT field and the swamp at home. I say river, but it is more a stream with pretensions, really.

When we arrived at the second house where Springy lives he went in and came out with a lump of metal that looked like a tiny woman for Bertie to see, and there was a lot of oohing and aahing for quite a while. Then it was out onto the dreadful road and more of the short lead horrors for Wills and me. He was so scared he just about strangled us every time a car came by. It proved so traumatic that when we eventually came through our gate and he took off the collars I could only stand and shiver for a good while, trying to regain my composure.

Thursday

This evening we had another session with the TV for some reason. Oh, I remember; it was about noisy things up in the air. The ones that make that particular noise often fly over the house; so why he needed to watch them yet again on the TV appears perverse in the extreme. He must be changing his habits, too, for that will be three times in one week that we have endured TV.

Just to make sure of nothing untoward happening again, I took the squeaky ball into the sitting room and played with it for a while because I felt frisky, and at least it won't stress my, currently, rather sore leg as that only really happens when playing roughly with Wills. However, there is just so much one can do on one's own with a ball, so after a short while I tucked it under the duvet I'd selected. Well, in due course, the TV was put out of its misery and we set out for the kitchen – me leaving the ball for the next time. He was having none of that and picked the ball up. So I took it from him and bought it to the safety of my bed.

For the past few days, Bertie has taken to disappearing for a couple of hours after the horses have come in. He always comes back smelling as he did when the large hospital swallowed him up. He must be going there, but for what I have not a clue. It doesn't happen every day, but regularly enough. Considering how structured his life is, it's very unsettling.

Friday

Ha! The other balls have come back, for the Housekeeper unearthed them when she was cleaning from some deep recess in the office. They could only have been hidden by one person, as no human would have the guile. Step forward Willow and take a bow!

We do seem to be learning an awful lot from each other, for I notice she has developed this 'invisible' streak as well now where she stands or walks just behind someone where they can't see her, even if they look over their shoulder. Whereas I've rather reverted to, sort of, almost jumping ups a bit when we greet people – mainly Bertie and the Housekeeper; and the Book-keeper gets it occasionally as well. It's too much trouble with anyone else. When he's playing the computer, I've also adopted Wills' trick of occasionally going up and laying my chin on his lap as that invariably attracts a distracted sort of fondling of the ears – his lap is at a convenient height and I am also particularly ticklish there. It also tells me he is still breathing. Willow, on the other hand, has finally learned how to smile, although it's presently more of a deathly grimace.

The Housekeeper is becoming slightly tight-lipped about the dirt the pair of us spread around the house; and she is particularly incensed that I seem to be shedding hair when neither of us should moult. However, she does concede that it is nothing compared to her doggy-dog. All it is, actually, is me losing the layer of coarse hair I acquired in my past, rough life. How can I tell her? Oh the irritation of not being able to talk human. I just stood and gave her my broadest smile and innocent doe eyed 'over-the-shoulder' look instead and that mollified her enough for a stroke, tickle and treat. It always works.

No sign of a walk for he was gallivanting on his normal Friday moonlighting stint. My leg is really playing up again, for at mucking-out time the bundle with Wills, accompanied by an awful lot of barking, was so energetic it left her panting for once and inevitably did my leg in. I wonder if my second home could take my bad leg off.

Saturday

Today was rather fun. We'd barely finished our measly breakfast and he was out the door and attacking a mole hill that invaded the lawn last night - this seems to involve a spade, thick leather gloves and some really foul-smelling pellets. This early morning activity was quite unlike his normal indolent self.

With the mole hill sorted, he then started dispersing the spoil tips from Wills' mining activities; and this seems to involve shoving bricks down the shafts and then filling it all up with soil. That took no less than six barrow-loads of mole hill earth from the BWT field into which we looked longingly; but he was VERY careful to open and close the front gate with each barrow load. Still, as it was an overcast but mild day we loved bundling, running and then just helping him – in my case, draping myself elegantly across the mound with face wreathed in a smile. Willow's contribution was rather more hands on - which didn't go down at all well.

Oh, the clod hopper managed to step on my bad leg, so I yelped piteously and hung it in dire agony. That produced a torrent of concern until I, unhelpfully, espied a pheasant strutting its stuff at the far end of the bird bath lawn and lit off at high speed to do the necessary. For some reason his stepping on my bad leg seemed to make the gaminess go away and as I was also feeling very frisky....

With the pheasant successfully despatched - now, when I say 'despatched', I don't mean 'caught', for the stupid bird didn't know the rules of the game, and flew away. So, 'despatched' then; and I went back to the almost sun bathing on the mound until we heard the gate, and saw the funny car with the back-to-front works. It was the relation from far away, who spent the next hour running in and out the house taking clothes up and bringing others down from the mystery room.

We finally waved her goodbye, and it was back to ministering to the lawns. He started quartering them with a muck fork in hand, finding all our #2's that he'd missed on his regular forays in that direction.

Now, Bertie is not the most observant creature. I have seen him search ever more frantically for his pen while all the time he was holding it. So, it goes without saying that even though Wills and I have our favourite spots, there was quite a bit of work involved in the crap-clearing.

Finally he fired up the screaming monster that belches smoke. It ate the grass and spat it out the side in a steady stream. After he'd finished, it all looked far neater and had totally changed the character of the garden. I couldn't resist that neat green sward, and there is not the slightest doubt it improved the going enormously; also as bits of undigested grass stuck between our pads, we were able to give the Housekeeper more work for we managed to distribute stray wodges of grass throughout the house. Reluctant to admit it, but that was a transformational job, and we finally came in for tea feeling very satisfied.

Well he'd just boiled the kettle, when the back door opened and there were the Nephew and Slobber Chops. I was so glad to see the Nephew that my tail nearly came off welcoming him; yes, I was that pleased! Well this meant we now knew he'd not do anything unpredictable, for they'd sit and gabble at the kitchen table and, sure enough, that is what happened but Slobber Chops was patently disinclined to do anything with us so we went outside and had a bundle, run, bundle and then a mighty run mainly based on the mound and bird bath areas for they can be seen from the kitchen.

Part of the fun of running is to an audience. We just felt so pleased with the sunshine. At one moment I decided on a breather - lying on the side of the mound whilst Wills filled the time by altering some of his mornings filling efforts. Finally, came in to find that Slobber Chops had done his doggy-dog thing and polished off all our nuts and water – and what a mess he left. Mind you, he probably needs it for it is some time since we last saw him and he has matured (grown big and fat) a lot. I don't think that I'd like to cross him on a dark night. He also started taking an interest in the balls, so I removed them and put them out of harm's way. Where, I can't remember, but no doubt they will return in due course.

SC and the Nephew soon went and, of course, mucking-out was out of the question so we went down to the stables and got the feed and hay in. Then as we came up the steps from the stables to bird bath, the clumsy oaf tripped over me and stepped on my ex-gammy leg again. The pain was excruciating and it undid all the previous good work.

Sunday

Here's an odd thing, for a recent visitor insisted that I was, in her words, "an alpha" but that cannot be, for I've never heard anyone call me 'my alpha' and everyone else seems to think I'm a greyhound. She must have muddled me up with another sort of dog. Mind you, she plainly didn't know what she was on about, for apparently Willow is a gamma – another unknown breed. It's all very strange.

I suppose that he'd been fired by yesterday's efforts for, while he allowed us to play to our hearts content, he bashed around the garden. This time, it started and rather ended with him trying to fire up the quad bike; but as it had not been loved since last summer, it was in a huff and refused to co-operate. So, in frustration, he did the double load of mucking-out which took an absolute age to finish.

Then he rushed in, donned smart clothes and shot out the house. As the car wasn't involved it must have been somewhere close but, obviously, we hadn't been invited. He came home in a very jolly mood – not jolly enough to take us for a walk, though, for he had another go at the holes he'd missed yesterday – told you he's not all that observant! This time he went to the oblong field for the mole hill earth, and I tended to stay with him, but Wills went haring off and was nowhere to be seen when he whistled for her. She had found the NW Passage into the BWT field again, and, after much frantic whistling eventually came back at a great lick. Now he'll spend hours thinking how to block that very large gap for it is a full-field-length-long gap.

Then it was quad bike's turn once more but it really was in a temper and refused point blank. Bertie finally left it attached to a load of flex to show it he really does care. We await the final outcome with interest.

Then the Nephew turned up with Slobber Chops for the second day running for they had been for a walk in our not so favourite slippery slope place. Strange, for we don't see him for weeks and weeks and then they turn up two days in a row. Well I was polite to SC and allowed him to wander around the garden, but when we came in to join Bertie and the Nephew, (who were already sitting at the table gabbling away), Willow turned very nasty whenever he made any move towards our beds.

Finally SC did manage it, and lifted an unused bone which he took into the passage indoors and gnawed. I really was not having that for it is OUR bone so when SC wasn't looking I quietly lifted it and took it outside, but the stupid mutt followed and regained possession. Well I came back to bed but Willow made sure to guard me against the intruder by spreading out right at the front. He then came in to check on his master so took the opportunity to go and retrieve the bone which I then put at the back of my bed out of temptation's way. Willow was now in full 'possessive' mode and again placed herself defensively between SC and me snarling at his every move. In due course the Nephew and SC left and I was mightily relieved, for the atmosphere had become quite poisonous. Willow felt the same, for when coming back from opening the gate for them, she skipped around like a new born lamb in relief.

You're probably wondering how I know the days. Well, it is quite simple really for, if you remember, I told you he is a creature of habit (except in the walks department). Thursday is the day the Bookkeeper comes; Saturday is shopping for the week – for him, not for us, as ours tends to come from the big barn right out in the country on his way home from work; Friday, of course, he moonlights; and Sunday is the day when he acts out a strange ritual.

Now we have things in each room that hit their bells at regular intervals, and every Sunday after the horses have come in, he goes to each, opens up its innards and pokes around winding them up. Then, when they are all wound and with their innards still exposed he rushes around adjusting the pointers, and, lo! After that they all strike their bells at almost the same moment. The combined noise is absolutely cacophonous. The one in the hall passage is particularly loud.

Then, as the week goes by some of them start to drag their heels until the following Sunday morning when this bell ringing takes some time as each decides to wake up and do its duty. It happens every Sunday, regular as clockwork. Willow is brilliant, for she knows what we should be doing or what is going to happen next by the number of times the bells sound. Now *that's* clever.

Bundling.

CHAPTER 10

Monday

I think that in passing I may have mentioned the six cottages on the farm. Well, they are in two terraces. The one overlooking the oblong field has a nice old couple who have lived here since before my great great great grandparents were even born. They're a gentle pair, although he has been ill for some time, and we often see a flashing ambulance outside. Attached to them is a very young couple + baby + a spitting small furry that we never see; and they have noisy cluckers for we hear them every morning when out for the morning ablution amble. They only came at around the time that Wills and I did, but they are very friendly and their home is both loving and welcoming.

The other four cottages are down and sliding into the yard containing the chichi offices which we pass every time we go in or out in the car, so I'm not really too sure about the people who live there, except for the first cottage for its back door is by our front gate. In it lives another gentle old lady who once had a sight hound and has lived here as long as the old couple, but she keeps to herself. She and the old couple are friends and always look very smart when they go out. Old school smart, for he never leaves his front door without wearing a tie, jacket, beautifully polished shoes, and, usually, a hat – even if it is only to potter in their immaculate garden.

From the odd glimpse of the other three cottages as we go past, there appear to be a frowning man with at least one Golden Hair and Floppy Ears that looks like a young Biddy, the dog, not the man. He seems to be related to Livery for he sometimes comes and talks to her. He also has two small spitting Furries who regularly invade our garden. We both go after them, but the stupid animals jump on top of the board fencing just out of reach where they then taunt us. I tend to be going so fast, that I invariably crash into the fence which does my leg no good but one day.....

Next door to him lives another man who we have yet to see, for he works strange hours; but he has a Large Black and Tan with long tail for that sometimes runs up and down the drive and we hear it barking an awful lot. The end cottage is right in amongst the chichi offices and sprouts pot plants everywhere. They even invade the chichi offices as well as the old pig sty where all the farm bins are kept. The person who lives there walks with a large stick and tends towards the black looks when we are around.

As to the chichi offices I really cannot tell you much except that the big black barn seems to have an awful lot of vans that come throughout the day either loaded with or taking away cardboard boxes by the score. As their door is often open I called in once and they were very friendly + there was an awful lot to investigate. All the other offices seem to sit there brooding mysteriously. We never see anyone, but their powerful and snarling cars glare out until its 'go home time' when they all roar away and leave us in blissful peace. Well that's the farm taken care of. Of course, it is no longer a working farm, except for the large tractor that comes and empties our muck trailer once a month and the odd load of belching, clanking machinery that sometimes tends to our fields.

Having forgotten about the quad bike he went and took the flex away and then, after a very long time which seems to include having the odd fag, it finally burst into life. He left it for a while to chunter to itself and then turned it off. What a lot of effort for such a paltry outcome.

Tuesday

Today was quite glorious with the sun blazing out of a cloudless sky but there was just enough chill to remind us not to put the coats away just yet. McGoo came home and immediately started filling some of Wills' past mining efforts that had escaped him twice already. I draped myself on the mound watching for it is my favourite place as it gets the full sun, cuts out the wind and I have a commanding view of the place – including the all important front gate. Wills had retired indoors after an altercation with him when she started digging under his nose. She stayed in a foul temper for the rest of the day and totally refused to play in any way.

There is just so much one can take watching someone standing over holes, and as I felt full of beans, went and got the squeaky ball. Came back and challenged him to play, but he wouldn't. I don't think he knows how to play, you know. So I half heartedly played for a bit, but Wills heard it squeaking and came out, grabbed it, and played with it herself for a while. When she stopped I picked it up and put it back in my bed. She is pretty offhand about such matters but I got my own back when he gave us our afternoon dental sticks for quickly gulped mine down then appropriated hers and ate it out on the mound. Normally we don't steal off each other but she had stolen my ball so I retaliated.

A strange thing then happened; for a small lorry rolled up, and a very big man got out. Bertie became very excited and directed the very big man to take the large slab of stone off the back and heave it to the far end corner of the terrace where it was left sticking flat out onto the terrace straight across our short cut over the wall to the side lawn. He pronounced himself satisfied but it was in quite the wrong place to be a step. Neither was it very high, so hopeless on that score as well. He may be satisfied, but we're not, for it is just one more unnecessary hazard cluttering up the place. It is useless, a safety hazard and not even nice to look at. A plain, flat piece of stone; he's not all that bright, is he?

Willow still in a filthy mood, and when the horses came in decided to start a not particularly gentle rumble - all snarls and snapping. In trying to avoid her, did my leg in again – only temporarily though, for it was fine by bed time.

Wednesday

I think that spring may finally have arrived, for today at least, because the sting has gone and it soon warms up to gloriously sunny days. Likewise, my gammy leg also seems to have lost its sting for, aside from yesterday evening, I only feel the occasional twinge when swerving violently. Not enough of a twinge to either limp or dangle it for sympathy though.

Today the Housekeeper arrived with a slab of rainbow-coloured stuff on a plate. The warehouseman also paid a visit, for he'd collected some horse feed in his van; and, also, the salesman turned up to mend a curtain holder that I'd accidently knocked out of the wall. They all sat down and devoured the rainbow stuff to much lip-smacking and we were even given a couple of very tiny bits to sample. It was scrumptious and fishy. Then Housekeeper disappeared into the dining room and clattered about behind the closed door; both episodes can only signal one thing – another lunch party.

It was particularly warm so when he came home, rather than resurrect the belching grass eating monster for another go on the lawns, he loaded us into the car and off we went to the hill with the big building on top for a VERY overdue walk. Out of laziness, we did the skirting-around-the-sides one rather than up to the big building, only he varied it and explored a path that we'd never been down previously, so it took twice as long. As he puffed around he had to sit on a dead tree for a while to recover as well as cool down, for he is still dressed for the cold, but this allowed us to explore a little further afield. Happily, he forbore to light up.

After a while we fell in with a couple of young chaps walking their model cars. The cars were very obedient for they went to heel superbly, even though they found the deep sand heavy going. I rather felt that a bundle with one of them could be in order but all the car did was roll onto its back and spin its wheels ineffectually. Total wash out.

We enjoyed both the walk and sun a lot, except that to our consternation, Wills disappeared for rather a long time at one point. Because I have become worried about Bertie wandering off aimlessly, I have rather taken to keeping him within reach but from today's episode it seems that I'll need to keep an eye on Wills as well. Someone has to keep the show on the road and he's far too scatterbrained to manage it.

Came home and lay on the mound for a most enjoyable and well deserved sleep in the sun. At last her rotten mood has lifted, so we also had a slight bundle and run.

Thursday

Well this morning we woke to overcast skies; but it was so warm that, like yesterday, the back door was left open. I just felt that life could not get any better and skipped or ran everywhere with my tail registering my feelings loud and clear. Lots of mini bundles with Wills and, for once, thoroughly enjoyed putting the horses out. In for usual derisory breakfast and then it was out to the mound and more bundles with Wills until she decided to do some gardening, so came in and collected squeaky ball to play with on the lawn. However, an overwhelming desire to re-test my bed overcame me, so I did just that – with a huge grin across my face until total lethargy intervened. It is just so nice to feel 100% and content with life. Think I've even forgiven the clod hopper for treading on my once gammy leg.

Wonders never cease! When he got back from work it was into the car and out to our favourite area – the cricket pitch, woods and heath. This time, it was a bit of a meander and we eventually ended up on the heath. Now, I should say that while the cricket pitch is on flat ground it is on top of the hill which slopes away as the heath takes over, but at that point there is a stunning view for miles and miles to some hills so far away that they are often invisible. Just the other side of them is the sea. It is a view that only locals know about. However, there is a large carved wood arty 'thingy' scarring the sky line. It makes a rather OTT pee post, and is used as one by all the local dogs.

When we got to the arty 'thingy' we fell in with a young man and his beautifully groomed Furry Black and White. I went up and made my mark as one does to all passing strangers and found him, the FB&W, to be as reserved as I. The more we probed, the more we liked each other for we both felt that doggy-dogs are a bit, how to say it politely, *ordinaire*. I felt that here was someone it was worth cultivating a friendship with, even though a blind man could see he wasn't built to run. Wrong build and far too furry for that as he was even feeling warm in this mild temperature, so we contentedly pottered along with Wills going off and doing whatever she does do on her own, while Bertie and the owner sat on a bench and talked. In due course the owner's fiancée joined the throng. So it wasn't long or arduous, but a very enjoyable walk. As he is a local, I hope that we meet the FB&W again because I really enjoyed his mature company.

CHAPTER 11

Saturday

It was just as I suspected for we went through the usual Saturday routine that presages a lunch party with the House-keeper bustling in loaded with bags and plates, including the rainbow fishy stuff, and then turning the kitchen into a hell-hole of activity, while he retired to the sitting room with the paper.

The first guest to arrive was driving an identical car to ours, only light blue; and out got a beaming smile, followed by a most attractive lady. She must have been very important for Bertie, while effusive, was also deferential. She also must like driving fast, for people only have our type of car because they like driving fast.

We'd hardly got over the arrival of the important, smiling lady, when a jolly and *extravagant* couple appeared in the tiniest car that I have ever seen; and they appeared to know the smiling lady, as did the next couple who pitched up at almost the same moment in one of those vast red jobbies with a snarling face. There was lots of air kissing and 'darling' flying around of course. The final couple arrived in a big black car which is just what we should have, for it was an absolute pantechnicon. It had all the makings of a good party.

As a punctilious host I circulated and tried to entertain them but, apart from a polite stroke, they ignored me and universally LOVED Wills with 'so pretty' 'oh she's adorable' (the she extravagant) 'what a beautiful dog' etc. etc. It was totally nauseating and I felt like vomiting. Well, that is until the dining room opened its door, when Wills retired to her boudoir, and I went into the usual mode of inspecting everything including the low pudding table – it's really convenient that my head is at exactly table-height for I then circulated quietly on a guest-by guest-basis as a conscientious Butler would in the past.

Ended up lying in the optimum spot where I could keep tabs on any comings and goings, because people are so untidy in their movements. I was only tripped over the once, sending a full plate of main course flying – that didn't matter for Wills heard the crash, came in and we cleared most of it up. We left the Housekeeper to finish off the detail, and thank goodness we are overstocked with roller towels for they are used for everything including my unauthorised ablutions. Trouble is, that the dining room is just that bit too tight to squeeze in a socialising dog as well as the guests.

After lunch, Bertie bored everyone by explaining his artworks one-by-plodding-one. Happily, that meant that I could keep them tidily in one room by lying across the doorway except that they then started stepping over me as people suddenly remembered they had pressing appointments elsewhere, and left rather hurriedly. Closing the gate after the last departure we then had something to eat ourselves and a mini-bundle on the big lawn until Wills started mining her favourite shaft again so I took the squeaky ball out for some air. For the second day running, any thoughts about a walk were, of course, out of the question.

When I say 'we had something to eat' what happens is that I watch Wills having her fill. Then, when she has finished, I get up and lie by the dish for my part of the meal. We don't like eating at the same time and it's good manners to defer to her anyway. It's different for lunch and breakfast where we each have our own dishes and then we do eat side by side, although, before starting, I always look over to check that she has the right amount of food – for he can be sloppy on that score.

In the evening we were deserted as he went out for a long time yet again. Judging by the eons that passed it must have been with Arty, as no one else holds him up that long.

Sunday

Oh, I don't think that I have mentioned it, but Wills has taken against her bed. It may have something to do with his endless tinkering for he decided to reduce the icicle that cuts straight to it by inserting a wedge of cardboard between bed and chopping table. To me, it makes her bed much more of a nest but she does not like it one little bit, so she's taken to sleeping everywhere but there. It's rather disquieting, for life has become 'untidy' as I cannot keep tabs on them both.

At least his conscience had struck, for Bertie *did* take us for a long ride in the car and we eventually decanted in a big sandy car park surrounded by enticing woods. Off we went into the woods and it was really interesting for there was a marshy lake which a couple of passing BBTs dived into, almost, but not quite, followed by Wills; steep hills up which he manfully struggled; then a great heath where we could run as far as the eye could see but with stunning views to the far distance. Naturally the place was riddled with interesting smells to investigate.

At every turn, there were three or four path options and we seemed to wander aimlessly at first; but gradually a pattern emerged for he did rather opt for the one to the right every time. At the top of a particularly gruelling hill was a bench onto which he flopped to get back his breath, while we started talking to the hordes of dogs that mysteriously appeared from every point of the compass. One felt that this must be a sort of canine Mecca, there were so many.

Both of us had our work cut out being sociable, but they were universally doggy-dogs and, apart from scampering around in circles, not one had the faintest clue about running. I noticed that the owners weren't particularly friendly either – very typical of town people. They all had the air of being in a private cocoon and wanting to keep themselves to themselves. It proved to be a very long walk and when we got back to the car I felt too fatigued to even manage the ramp. He just HAD to lift us both in and we promptly lay down and went to sleep. Now Wills has never ever done that before, in case she might miss something, so even *she* must have felt the strain.

We were pleased to see our beds and slept very well.

Monday

And the weather was glorious so we were rather hoping it may be a walk day – and it was. We went to our favourite: the cricket pitch, woods and heath. We started by going into the butterfly field where we had a burn-up chasing a mythical furry that Wills thought she had seen. We went out through the trap, and turned off to the right straightaway, and I am jolly glad we did for it took us to the bottom of the commercial woods because we hadn't been there before, and we met Game. Now you may remember that I said she had smelt of dog the first time we met? Well the smells were there walking with her – a small brown BCLTH and a multi-coloured BSH. I was relieved to see that the BCLTH looked normal rather than the dolled-up hussy we had met on the big hill walk. We exchanged the usual courtesies but no more as neither of them were 'our' sort of dog, i.e. runners – and parted.

A short while later a very large tractor came towards us with an equally large log trailer in tow. It then parked itself just near where we were and the trailer moved the hoist it had at its front and lifted a cut tree and neatly placed it on its back. I think the man in the tractor was actually working it, but both Bertie and I were transfixed for it was all so neat and efficient.

Just as we arrived back at the car I espied a type of dog I've never seen before. His body and head were about the same size as mine BUT he had such short legs that his chest almost scraped the ground, and it was all emphasised by having long silky hair. As he walked, he looked like a floor mop floating along. He took ten strides to my one. Well, I liked the Short Legs Long Hair very much so attached myself to him and his owner in my vague way, quite disregarding the calls from the car and had to be retrieved with the usual nuclear option (my lead).

Once home, we tended to stay out but I *did* notice Bertie's beloved cap that goes everywhere with him; so decided to play with that on the mound and passed a most agreeable half hour. It rapidly reduced to a sodden mess and he was NOT amused.

Tuesday

For someone who purports to have no territorial inclinations I have noticed that I am becoming materialistic. Last night he came down for the usual midnight snack, and, rather than ignoring him as she normally does, Willow started kicking up her 'I want out' fuss so, very grumpily, he let us out and went back to feeding his face. During the long pee I remembered that last thing last night I'd taken the squeaky ball out for one and then rather forgotten it, so bought it back and tucked it safely into bed. In my languid way, the welfare of that ball is starting to pre-occupy me a lot which suggests I must be turning into a doggy-dog. How plebeian.

Wednesday

Today the worm turned for we had barely brought the horses in and he was into smart clothes and disappeared for a very long time. Eventually, he returned with Distinguished, let us out for the briefest moment and shot off again taking her home. I'd barely had time to gather my thoughts let alone do anything, so registered my protest in a positive way by doing the largest #2 that I could manage just by the back door so he'd be sure to step in it when he came in. He did.

Thursday

This morning it was very miserable and damp with a light drizzle. Not enough to leave you soaking, but just enough to be wet. But it was warm, so the morning walk proved a bit of fun, although I didn't do any actual running myself. Willow had a couple of little spurts, but I couldn't be bothered and was quite content to walk beside Bertie.

Then he came home from work early and opened a VAST parcel that had arrived; bought by the shy postman rather than the regular, cheerful one, who goes to 'Goff' a lot. Very boring, for it is a new ramp for me; but it appears to be heavier, trickier, and bigger than the one the dog trainer loaned us. Down to the car we all traipsed, and I will say one thing: it is twice as wide as the old one, but I was still NOT going to use it. Mind you, he got in a dreadful tangle opening and closing it, and it doesn't go in the back seat foot wells, which was where he vainly tried to stow it; so that can safely be consigned to the expensive failures bin! I wonder what poor sap will be landed with it, for dog ramps are not exactly the top of anyone's shopping list.

Back to the house and he started fussing around the kitchen taking out the toaster from its home on the shelf above my bed. Now I have never seen that being used before, as he normally uses the wire paddles on the AGA. Then a stream of goodies came out of the fridge, and, in due course up rolled a very charming young woman. They never stopped talking while they snuffled at the trough. They took so long, that it gradually dawned on us that any thoughts of a walk could be safely shelved. In fact, she was such an age going that he could barely get the mucking-out done before Livery arrived to bring the nags in. We both liked the charming young woman though, for she exuded the right vibes.

Friday

Well, the plain stone slab on the terrace does have a use after all. No sooner had he returned from his moonlighting than a pickup arrived driven by the excrescence man. In the back he had an excrescence just like the one on the wall at the front; only this is a lurid yellow rather than the violent orange of the other. First, some bricks were put under the slab to 'give it depth'. Well, a blind man can see that it was going *upwards*, so what was all this talk about *depth*? Then, the excrescence was bolted onto the stone slab, making another dense barrier for us to negotiate. One tangled heap of metal is bad enough, but two is beyond the pale. Of course, much oohing and aahing and after a while, the House-keeper turned up to look: while she liked it, she still split her sides laughing. I also registered my contempt by peeing on it. At least we'll not crash into it, for subtle it is not. It shouts 'look at me' VERY LOUDLY. Normally, when these arty things arrive there is a party to welcome them so suspect one must be in the offing.

Did I ever mention that I purr? Well, I do although not all that often; only when I am particularly content. It happened this morning, for, when we came in from putting the horses out Bertie gave me a passing stroke and found a tiny tuft of tangled hair - the aftermath of a nasty little nick from a passing rose bush. It would not untangle, so he got out his comb and teased it out, and I liked the attention so much I purred quietly while he was doing it.

For the third day running, walks were off the agenda but then, looking on the bright side, it hasn't stopped raining either. Willow is very restless. As compensation I took the squeaky ball out to the mound for an airing as it hadn't been out for a few days, and decided it should experience a burn-up. Not such a good idea though, for it badly interfered with my breathing, so it was quite a short spin. I was a bit careless putting it to bed for I accidently dropped it beside Willow's bed and she refused to let me have it back. I managed to rescue it later when she wasn't looking.

Saturday
The new ramp has disappeared so it must have found a willing victim!

Today was something of a red letter day on all counts for we had another lunch party. Oh, I'd better start at the beginning. It was a lovely sunny day and I felt that the squeaky ball-which has now lost its squeak-needed a little attention; so when we went out for our morning apology for an ablution, I took it. As I now had 'responsibilities', tended to ignore Wills and her phantom sighting; so let her roar off to the triangle field while I tended to the well being of the ex-squeaky ball. Finished by subjecting it to a blinding burst as we rushed back to welcome the cheerful Post Man, who was, as usual going to 'Goff' again.

I really do wonder where 'Goff' is as he does seem to go there an awful lot, even though nobody else does. We followed that by having a massive burn-up, which came to an abrupt end when I let out a mighty yelp as Wills stepped on my ex-gammy leg during one close encounter. Even though I hung it dramatically, not a blind bit of sympathy was forthcoming.

Then it was breakfast, horses out, morning muck-out for a change, and back to bed. Very strange behaviour but as there had been frequent visits to the bog during the night, all was obviously not so well, and I suppose it was to be expected.

Mid-morning the Housekeeper arrived. Well, we knew that was going to happen, for all week she had been in and out of the dining room, laying it out for a lunch. The usual mayhem ensued in the kitchen, while he fired up the gas-eating monster. About time too, for the lawns looked like a hay field.

The first guests arrived early and caught him napping, for he'd not yet got dolled-up; and that was when OUR party started. It was the nice lady from the Greyhound Rescue Centre and her husband, but without any dogs attached. Next off was an elegant dog just like me, but with long hair on his ears and tail. He started very diffidently but soon realised we had identical thought processes. Wills liked him a lot. Soon after came a very large dog, again just like me, but with very silky hair; and also, just like me he had found his home – except that he'd been a bit more proactive about it.

It was a mighty squeeze in the drawing room, what with eight people and four very excited dogs – two on leads, and most anxious to explore the strange surroundings. To defuse it, and to the slight consternation of the visitors' people, Bertie suggested that we should go outside for space to get acquainted, which is what happened. Leads off, and with an awful lot of barking and feinting, we instantly found that they liked bundling and running just as much as us. Mind you, Wills became quite snappy, establishing in their minds that this was OUR home – typical female!

Oh, we did have fun and as the door was open we spent the rest of the day alternating with burn-ups, bundling, or joining the humans in the dining room. I think that I've already mentioned that it's a bit of a squeeze in there so, as the office door was open, and Bertie was seated well in sight, both Wills and I tended to lie in there when recuperating, while the other two found impossibly tiny spaces near their owners in the dining room. I did notice that quite often the pair of them went out on their own, as they had oodles of excess energy to burn off. They also took to exploring the house with not a hair being turned by anyone, least of all Bertie – well the humans were used to our natural sight hound curiosity, even when each of us, bar Wills (have I? - oh, forget it!) inspected the goodies on the low table in the corner of the dining room. The very large one with the silky hair has a reputation for being a thief, but he took his cue from me and forbore to uphold his reputation.

It was all so agreeable that even Wills, who normally retires when there are lots of humans, stayed and enjoyed the party. In fact, she often led in the bundling department. It's just typical of her to have to oversee everything; she can be a real 'bossy boots' when in the mood, - but the other two endured it with good grace for we were all having such a ball.

I must say that the whole affair was fairly chaotic. As Bertie couldn't organise a piss-up in a brewery (it's usually the sensible Housekeeper and me who keep things on an even keel) and there were humans AND dogs to cope with, it almost overpowered even my legendary organisational abilities.

Finally the time came to go and, as we had an appreciative audience, it was one more monumental bundle followed by an around-the-garden burn-up, which, being the fastest, I led, of course. As they witnessed their dogs running in safety, the human appreciation of the spectacle was palpable. Car tail-gates down and both guests jumped into the one car, almost followed by Wills – but the lip was a mite too high for her. It was with enormous sadness that we waved them goodbye, for we never normally have dogs of our own to entertain. We adjudged the 'Sight Hound Lunch' a great success, and as we are both knackered, it's time for bed if you don't mind!

Sunday

This morning, the icy East wind had returned, but it was dry if overcast so felt very fit on the travesty of a morning walk. I even joined Wills with her usual phantom-sighting-run and as that got the blood flowing, we had a series of mini burn-ups coming back to the house. In for breakfast and realised that the squeaky ball hadn't been out so took it for a constitutional on the mound. Then squeaky and I, went back to bed. I like squeaky because it is predictable and I can keep it tidy although it will play if asked and, of course, it does protest if we are getting too rough, or I

accidently lie on it. It's easy to carry and best of all it doesn't take up too much space in bed. Actually, the very best thing of all is that it never tells me what to do. It needs constant protection from Wills of course. She's so conventional for she has her own balls, but takes not a blind bit of notice unless someone's throwing them.

Bertie was particularly indolent this morning; first bashing into the bloody computer, then a riffle through yesterday's paper, then a series of boring phone calls as he vainly tried to find someone to go for that long overdue walk with us. So there *was* hope.

Hope dashed, and so, before starting on the garden, he took a couple of pots of homemade Marmalade (not made by him I might add) to both the old and young couples in the top cottages, being careful to close the gate so we stayed in the drive. I managed to get through the so called 'dog proofing' and join him but declined to show him how I got through. Now he'll try to worm that out of me, but it's my little secret and if he thinks I'm going to show him he'd better think again.

It was very interesting, for I could explore the young couple's garden and, of course, while satisfying my curiosity was deaf to his calls and whistles. It seems that they have a lodger, for he was sheltering under the outhouse enjoying a morning fag clothed in only his bath robe and bare feet. Not even jimjams – he must have been frozen.

Then, it was out to the lawns once more to <u>really</u> put paid to Wills' mining endeavours, and I have to say that he is becoming quite white and spiteful about them; and as Wills can be so thick and persistent at times, I feel that this will end in tears. The Arctic wind didn't help matters at all.

After that, it was the usual detailed quartering with the muck fork picking up all the crap he'd missed during the week, followed by the belching grass eater. He finished that way past lunch time and was knackered. Finally, we came in for lunch/tea and the Sunday ritual of the striking things, but not a sign of any consideration for our needs at all throughout the day, so we just had to make our own arrangements.

Things just cannot go on like this and I really do need to register a protest somewhere. A little reluctant to go to the Greyhound Rescue Centre, for he's showing all the signs of becoming broody again and if one rocks the boat too much we might be joined by more dogs, and as he can't cope with us that would never do.

Well, reminiscing and writing this has been fun and I do so hope that you have enjoyed sharing the window on Wills' and my life, but, people to see, things to do.

By the way, if you happen to live in a draught-free house with about 50 acres of lawn interspersed with clumps of trees and bushes, active children of a reasonable age, and are looking to lower the possibility of a coronary yourself, we are gregarious, quiet, (except when I am goading Wills into a bundle), good around the house, sleep an awful lot and eat little. Oh, and we don't moult much. A comfortable bed is a given of course. All enquiries welcome. Mind you, word of warning, you should get very chummy with a good Vet. Only for me, Wills doesn't use them.

Good bye.

Bandit

POSTSCRIPT

As some time has passed since my great scribble project, I am sure you'd like to know the current state of play. Well, first of all spring still hasn't arrived, even though British Summer Time has; and even the swallows have returned! The winds have been icier and more cutting than in January, and it is always raining, and if it's not, then it's drizzling. Yuk!

I feel so healthy and full of beans that it's spurt or bounce everywhere, and it's up and out at every opportunity. I can even, finally, run Willow into the ground. In the rear department my tail usually resembles a demented windscreen wiper. Of course, it goes without saying that my face is constantly split in half with a smile, for life just couldn't be better. Our bundles, always instigated by me I might add, are really energetic; and we've taken to sharing our beds.

Wills has given up mining and, taken to hunting instead. Her main areas are the canyon behind the stables and the laurel hedge: her bag to date being five BWTs. That hedge is worrying Bertie, for it is the Belgium to his Maginot Line onto the road, and he gets very twitchy. Incidentally, he's still not twigged how I can get through the front gate defences.

Rather like the bog rolls of yore, I've taken to gardening. The Warehouseman is bashing into it for its annual wash and brush-up; and the quad bike is working overtime. He doesn't seem to appreciate my efforts to help one little bit. In fact, he gets quite shirty; but happily, it's Wills who gets the flak. These being a classic case of "give a dog a bad name" of course.

It goes without saying that the change of times is playing havoc with my toilet arrangements.

No more crashing into the board fence either, for the adventurous Small Spitting Furry, who caused us such angst, was wandering in the road and a car ran it over. That's one aggravation less for the other is too timid to venture out alone.

Domestically, we still ricochet from one disaster to the next; the latest being yet another go at cooking tapioca – when the precious and irreplaceable little blue Poole Pottery container shattered in the intense heat of the top oven. He followed that by making a second batch, which came out all lumpy. He'll never learn of course, he's too senile for that, and why this perseverance with tapioca I ask? He decided that the printer had shot it, so bought a new one; but then the old one got over its sulk, and is now working again, but only AFTER he'd unpacked the new one and burnt all the packaging! He did turn over the utility room and, like Dr. Livingston, finally located the source of the worst icicle though. The remaining one is a mere zephyr.

On the squeaky ball front, there was an atmosphere so Bertie bought Willow one. It's smaller, squeakier and ovoid shaped – just perfect to take for an extended run, which I do all the time; for Wills may well snarl but she'll never actually *fight* for it – so there's now even *more* of an atmosphere.

Yesterday I took it for our morning walk and it obviously loved the burn-ups, for it squeaked away like mad all the time. Then he pulled a fast one on us by buying her an even nicer squeaking bone which, obviously, I instantly purloined. Now there is a dilemma: which squeaky to claim? Think I'll leave her the ovoid and concentrate on the bone; or perhaps the bone and let her have the ovoid. Wills is being very difficult about the whole thing. The original squeaky ball, of course, is absolutely last week, and lying unloved in a corner of the kitchen.

Oh, and we have found a way to get to the commercial woods and butterfly sanctuary without having to go in the car. It does involve a very long climb up the lane out of the village though. We discovered this Southern passage with Slobber Chops one Sunday and he, Bertie I mean not SC, has now become obsessed with it, even though that Eiger north face start knocks him out.

Well that's about it Ta ta.